Unit Four Resource Book

McDougal Littell

THE LANGUAGE OF LITERATURE

GRADE NINE

McDougal Littell
A HOUGHTON MIFFLIN COMPANY
Evanston, Illinois • Boston • Dallas

McDougal Littell Inc. grants permission to the classroom teacher to reproduce these copymasters as needed.

ISBN 0-395-96798-8

5 6 7 8 9 10 11 – CKI – 09 08 07 06 05 04 03

Unit Four All in the Family

Family and Community Involvement

OPTION 1 Discussing

Conduct a Family Conference

- **Purpose** To plan and conduct a conference with family members to discuss how to resolve conflicts
- **Connection** The selections in Unit Four explore how family members relate to one another.
- **Materials** writing paper, a pen or pencil, a ruler (optional)
- **Activity** To improve communication and find ways to resolve conflicts, especially among siblings, many families hold regular conferences. During such conferences, family members air their differences, make requests, and plan events. Work with your teenager to develop a general plan for a family conference. You may wish to involve other family members in deciding on an agenda or items to discuss, using a form like the one shown. Then set up a time for the conference when everyone can attend.

Family Conference Agenda

Item 1: ______________________________

Plan of Action or Resolution: ______________________________

____

Item 2: ______________________________

Plan of Action or Resolution: ______________________________

____

Item 3: ______________________________

Plan of Action or Resolution: ______________________________

____

Unit Four All in the Family

Family and Community Involvement

OPTION 2 **Writing**

Write an Anecdote About the Family

- **Purpose** To recall and write or record memorable and funny family anecdotes
- **Connection** Some of the selections in Unit Four describe touching, emotional, and sometimes funny episodes from family life.
- **Materials** writing paper, a pen or pencil, a ruler *or* a tape recorder and cassette tape, family photos from remembered events (optional)
- **Activity** Some of the most memorable events in a family's history are those that are touching or funny. Talk with your teenager about events that are especially memorable. Encourage your teenager to write down or tape-record those anecdotes, or ask another family member to do so. You might look through family albums to see if any pictures were taken of the events you recall. To help you choose the most memorable events, you may wish to use a form like the one shown to recall facts and take notes.

Family Anecdote

When: ______________________________

Where: ______________________________

Who: ______________________________

What Happened: ______________________________

Why It Is Memorable: ______________________________

Family and Community Involvement

OPTION 3 Viewing

Watch a Video About Families

- **Purpose** To view a film that depicts family relationships
- **Connection** The selections "The Scarlet Ibis" and "Marine Corps Issue" explore relationships among family members.
- **Materials** a TV and VCR, a film that tells a story about family relationships, writing paper, a pen or pencil, a ruler
- **Activity** In many of today's films that deal with interactions among family members, people often recognize experiences their own families have had. Select a film that centers on a family, such as *Parenthood* or *Avalon,* both of which should be available at most video stores. After watching the film with your teenager, talk about the memorable experiences the family members shared and how they solved problems or resolved disagreements. Discuss your opinions of the family's solutions. You and your teenager may wish to record some of your ideas on a chart like the one shown.

Film Title:____________________________

Family Conflict/ Problem	What Happened	How Resolved	Your Opinion of the Family's Solution

The Scarlet Ibis

James Hurst

Summary

Setting: A cotton farm in North Carolina, 1914–1918
The narrator is a young boy. His brother Doodle is small and sickly. Everyone thinks Doodle will die. He lives, but he is weak. The narrator is disappointed with Doodle. Whenever the narrator goes out to play, his mother makes him take Doodle with him. So the narrator sometimes scares Doodle, just to be mean. Yet, he also shares his favorite place, a swamp, with Doodle.

Doodle is five. The narrator is embarrassed that Doodle can't walk yet. He decides to teach Doodle to walk. By fall, they have a surprise for the family: Doodle can walk across the room. The narrator doesn't want Doodle to be "different" when he starts school next fall. He pushes Doodle to run, swim, climb trees, fight, and row a boat.

One day, the family discovers an unusual red bird–a scarlet ibis–in a tree near their house. The bird dies. Upset, Doodle buries it in the garden. Later that day, the narrator makes Doodle row the boat to shore. A storm begins. It is raining hard. The narrator is angry that Doodle is still weak and different. He runs home, leaving Doodle behind. Then he goes back for Doodle. Doodle has fallen and died.

Name ______________________ Date ______________________

The Scarlet Ibis (page 592)

Active Reading SkillBuilder

Drawing Conclusions About the Narrator

To make an inference, readers look at details and make logical guesses about what they mean. To **draw a conclusion,** readers combine these inferences with what they already know. An active reader of fiction is constantly making inferences and drawing conclusions about what the characters are doing or thinking and what motivates them. As you read this selection, use the chart to record three passages from which you can infer something about the narrator. Using these inferences, draw a conclusion about him.

Passage	Inference
"It was bad enough having an invalid brother, but having one who possibly was not all there was unbearable."	The narrator is insensitive to others and is thinking only of himself.

Conclusion

Name ______________________ Date ______________

The Scarlet Ibis (page 592)

Literary Analysis SkillBuilder

Theme

A **theme** is the central idea or message in a work of fiction. It is a perception about life or human nature that the writer shares with the reader. Ways to look for a theme in a story include:

- reviewing what happens to the main character. (Does the character change during the story? What does the character learn about life?)
- skimming key phrases and sentences that say something about life or people in general.
- thinking about the story's title. (Does it have a meaning that could lead to a major theme?)
- remembering that a story may have more than one theme.

Go back through the story and list statements that go under the headings in the chart below.

What Narrator Learns	Key Passages	Importance of Title

Follow Up: Write the themes you find in complete sentences. Compare your themes with those of classmates.

Name ______________________________ Date ______________________

The Scarlet Ibis (page 592)

Words to Know SkillBuilder

Words to Know

careen	exotic	imminent	invalid	precariously
doggedness	heresy	infallibility	iridescent	reiterate

A. Decide which word from the word list belongs in each numbered blank. Then write the word on the blank line on the right.

No, "Misisipi" isn't how to spell the state. To be
Correct you must (1) both *s*'s and the *p*. ______________ (1)

That vase is priceless! Children, stop!
Do not (2) about the shop! ______________ (2)

When I begin to fidget, you can tell
My boredom means my (3) farewell. ______________ (3)

To anyone who knows geography,
"The world is flat" is simply (4)! ______________ (4)

Spilled oil isn't lovely, but when it reflects the light,
It makes an odd and interesting, (5) sight. ______________ (5)

My parents said no when I asked for a pup.
I kept pleading as days and weeks passed.
At last they gave in when I didn't give up,
So, my (6) paid off at last! ______________ (6)

B. Fill in each blank with the correct word from the word list.

1. If you spell ______________ wrong, it's a trait you don't have!
2. The Korean dish kim-chee is as ______________ to a Canadian as Canadian bacon is to a Korean.
3. We moved in with my ______________ grandparents to take care of them when their health failed.
4. A straw hat would sit on your head ______________ during a windstorm.

C. Imagine that ten years have passed since Doodle's death. What advice do you think the narrator would give a child who was in a situation that was similar to the one the narrator had been in while Doodle was alive? Write down that advice, using at least **three** of the Words to Know.

Name ______________________________ Date ______________

The Scarlet Ibis (page 607)

Grammar SkillBuilder: Prepositional Phrases

Key Concept: Writers employ prepositional phrases to add details to their writing. Prepositional phrases can help establish setting, mood, and tone.

Prepositional Phrases

A **prepositional phrase** consists of a preposition, its object, and any modifiers of the object. The object of a preposition is always a noun, a pronoun, or a group of words used as a noun. Prepositional phrases can function as adjectives or adverbs. Adjective phrases modify nouns and pronouns; adverb phrases modify verbs, adverbs, or adjectives. To avoid confusion, prepositional phrases are usually placed close to the words they modify.

"The five o'clocks **by the chimney** still marked time, but the oriole nest **in the elm** was untenanted and rocked back and forth **like an empty cradle.**"

"I pulled the go-cart **through the sawtooth fern, down to the green dimness** where the palmetto fronds whispered **by the stream.**"

Activity

Rewrite these sentences, adding a prepositional phrase to modify each underlined noun, verb, or adjective. The prepositional phrase should answer the question in parentheses. If you wish, you can begin your phrase with the preposition in italics. Underline the prepositional phrase.

Example: The action in "The Scarlet Ibis" takes place (when? *during*) on a cotton farm (where? *in*).

Rewritten: The action in "The Scarlet Ibis" takes place during World War I on a cotton farm in the South.

1. Until he learned to crawl, Doodle stayed on the rubber sheet (where? *on*).
2. Daddy built Doodle a go-cart and I carted him (where? *around*).
3. I dragged poor Doodle (how? *in*) (where? *to*).
4. One day I took Doodle (where? *into*) and made him touch the coffin (how? *with*).
5. When I first started to teach him to walk, he fell each time (how? *like*).
6. We surprised the family when Doodle walked (where? *across*) and sat in his chair.
7. He had practiced walking every day that summer. (where? *in*).
8. That summer many trees (where? *in*) were uprooted (how? *by*).
9. The beautiful dying bird (which one? *with*) must have been blown in (how? *by*).
10. I ran (where? *toward*) in the rain, and when I went back I found Doodle had fallen (where? *beside*).

Name ______________________ Date ______________

The Scarlet Ibis (page 592)

Selection Quiz

Recall the events in Hurst's short story. Then answer the questions in phrases or sentences.

1. Early in the story, why does the narrator feel burdened by Doodle?

2. Why does Doodle cry the first time he sees Old Woman Swamp?

3. How does Doodle react to the scarlet ibis's death?

4. As they run home through the storm, why won't the narrator wait for Doodle?

5. At the end of the story, why does the narrator think of the scarlet ibis when he looks at his brother?

Name ______________________ Date ______________

Lineage/The Courage That My Mother Had (page 608)

Active Reading SkillBuilder

Drawing Conclusions About the Speaker

When reading a poem in which the **speaker** tells his or her thoughts in the first person, try to get an idea of who that person is. Make inferences based on what you read and then **draw a conclusion** based on those inferences. While reading the two poems, use the chart below to write anything you can conclude about the speakers, such as their values, feelings, or sense of identity. Remember that the speaker of a poem is not necessarily the poet.

"Lineage"		
Speaker's Values	**Speaker's Feelings**	**Speaker's Sense of Identity**

"The Courage That My Mother Had"		
Speaker's Values	**Speaker's Feelings**	**Speaker's Sense of Identity**

Name ______________________ Date ______________________

Lineage/The Courage That My Mother Had (page 608)

Literary Analysis SkillBuilder

Sound Devices

Part of the power of poetry comes from the poet's use of sound devices. These include rhyme and rhythm, **alliteration** (repetition of consonant sounds at the beginning of words), **repetition** (repeated words or phrases), and **assonance** (repetition of vowel sounds within words that don't rhyme). Look for examples of repeated sounds in the poems. Write them in the chart.

Alliteration	Repetition	Assonance
went with	*with her/with her*	

Follow Up: For each poem, describe how the sound devices enhance the experience of reading the poem.

Name ______________________ Date ______________

My Papa's Waltz/Grape Sherbet (page 613)

Active Reading SkillBuilder

Analyzing Sensory Details

The words and phrases that re-create sensory experience for the reader are often referred to as **sensory details.** Sensory details help the reader experience a poem to its fullest. As you read the poems, look for sensory details that seem particularly striking. Write them on the graphic below.

Sensory Details	
"My Papa's Waltz"	**"Grape Sherbet"**

Name ______________________________ Date ______________

My Papa's Waltz/Grape Sherbet (page 613)

Literary Analysis SkillBuilder

Imagery

Imagery is language that appeals to any of the senses. A poet uses imagery to bring a poem "inside" the reader; to help the reader see, hear, smell, taste, and feel what's being described. As you read, find as many images as you can that appeal to the senses. Write the images and passages you find on the chart below.

Senses	Images in "My Papa's Waltz"	Images in "Grape Sherbet"
Sight	mother's frown	
Hearing	pans falling	
Smell		
Taste		
Touch		

Follow Up: Think of a special memory associated with a family member or a close friend. Quickly sketch a picture to represent the memory. Draft a poem about the memory, using imagery to help the reader experience it. Share your poem with another student.

Marine Corps Issue

David McLean

Summary

Setting: Missouri, 1964–1984

Johnny recalls that his father kept three locked boxes in the shed. The boxes held things from his days as a Marine. Johnny's father was in Vietnam for the first years of Johnny's life. Johnny says his father is no longer in the Marines because his hands were crippled. His father has never talked about the war.

Johnny is sixteen. He sees a movie about the Vietnam War. He wants to know about his father's past. He begins to read about the war. Johnny decides to look inside the boxes in the shed. He finds old photos, uniforms, and a medal. The medal is for being wounded in action.

Johnny goes to a ballgame with his father. Johnny says that baseball is their closest connection.

The next day, Johnny opens the third box. He finds newspaper articles about his father. He was a prisoner of war, and his hands had been crippled by torture. His father walks into the shed. He is angry and crying. After that, however, Johnny's father sometimes talks about the war to him.

Name ______________________ Date ______________________

Marine Corps Issue (page 618)

Active Reading SkillBuilder

Recognizing Cause and Effect

Sometimes two events are related as **cause** and **effect**—that is, one event actually brings about the other. The first event in time is the cause; the second event is the effect. In "Marine Corps Issue," for example, the father has disabled hands (a cause). This condition forces him to retire from the Marines (an effect). As you read, use the chart to write down the effects that the war has on the narrator's father. Also note the effects that the war has on the family.

Effects of the Vietnam War	
On the Father	**On the Family**

Name ________________________ Date ____________

Marine Corps Issue (page 618)

Literary Analysis SkillBuilder

Flashback

A **flashback** is an account of a conversation, an episode, or an event that happened before the beginning of the story. At the beginning of "Marine Corps Issue," the narrator is a grown man. He tells the story in a series of flashbacks to different times in his life. On the chart below, identify some of the flashbacks in which the narrator as a young boy or as a teenager (Johnny) learns something about his father. Then write what he learns.

Flashback	What Johnny Learns About His Father

Name ______________________________ Date ______________

Marine Corps Issue (page 618)

Words to Know SkillBuilder

Words to Know

agitated	demeanor	devoid	grotesque	trepidation
animosity	deprivation	disjunction	intrigue	vulnerability

A. Decide which word from the word list belongs in each numbered blank. Then write the word on the blank line on the right.

Rhubarb and pickled eggs? I can't digest
A dish whose recipe is so (1)!
And I must ask, although it may be rude,
Why is your kitchen so (2) of normal food?

I could tell by my mother's disgusted (3)
She thought that my bedroom should be a lot cleaner.

The bridge, since the tornado hit, cannot perform its function.
It once connected to the land, but now there's a (4).

It's been three years since I have had a day for a vacation.
And I am getting cranky from this lengthy (5).
I think my nervous jumpiness might well have demonstrated
That too much work without a break can make one (6).

Just look at any baby deer and its fragility.
Now isn't that the picture of (7)?

My sister's baseball crazy, so the questions that (8) her
Are those about the records of each major Major Leaguer.

Each creaking, groaning sound at night
Fills me with (9).
It's tough to be the victim of
A good imagination!

"Why are your ears so big?" she asks.
"And how much do you weigh?"
My darling little neighbor
Has new questions every day.
And, every day, examples of her childish curiosity
Arouse in me strong feelings of the deepest (10)!

______________ (1)

______________ (2)

______________ (3)

______________ (4)

______________ (5)

______________ (6)

______________ (7)

______________ (8)

______________ (9)

______________ (10)

B. Imagine that Johnny had written a letter to explain to his father why he had broken into the locker boxes in the tool shed. Write a paragraph from that letter, using at least **four** of the Words to Know.

Name ______________________________ Date ______________

Marine Corps Issue (page 638)

Grammar SkillBuilder: Appositive Phrases

Key Concept: Writers employ appositive phrases to identify or clarify information about a person, place, thing, or idea. Using an appositive helps the flow of the writing by combining information that would otherwise be given in separate sentences.

Appositive Phrases

An **appositive** is a noun or pronoun that usually comes directly after another word in a sentence to identify or provide other information about the word. An **appositive phrase** consists of the appositive and all of its modifiers. Compare the following examples from David McLean's short story "Marine Corps Issue." Notice that the appositive phrase in the first example could be removed from the sentence without affecting the meaning of the sentence, and therefore is set off by commas. In the second example, however, the appositive phrase is essential—it gives the title of the movie.

Nonessential, Commas: "I could have been any child**, an adopted son,** were it not for my resemblance to him."

Essential, No Commas: "At sixteen I saw the movie ***Apocalypse Now.***"

Activity

Rewrite these sentences, adding an appositive phrase to provide more information about the underlined noun or pronoun.

Example: David McLean grew up in Granite City, Illinois.

Rewritten: David McLean grew up in Granite City, Illinois, a small town much like the fictional Stone City.

1. The first time I saw what was in the boxes was when Dad's friend came to visit.
2. The film opened Johnny's eyes to his father's history.
3. After seeing the film, Johnny went to the library and borrowed three books.
4. His summer project was to learn about the Vietnam War.
5. Johnny went to his sanctuary to read each day.
6. His mother begged Johnny not to make Dad think about his memories.
7. One day during that summer of drought, my brother and I drove by a withered cornfield.
8. I showed Joe *Great Expectations* and *Dispatches*.
9. The locks must have come with two keys.
10. The top tray contained family memorabilia.
11. In his platoon book Johnny found pictures of a younger, less tired version of his father.
12. Johnny's namesake was also pictured in the book.
13. One of the photos in the second box had an inscription on the back.
14. Father and son went to the Cardinals game.
15. Johnny's father only spoke of the war in brief, slow monologues.

Name ______________________ Date ______________

Marine Corps Issue (page 618)

Selection Quiz

Recall the events in McLean's short story and then answer the questions in one or two sentences.

1. When Johnny was a baby, why was his name changed from Charles to Jonathan?

2. When his father came home to live with the family, five-year-old Johnny quickly learned that it was important not to startle his father. Why?

3. Why did Johnny hide his books on Vietnam?

4. After Johnny found the Purple Heart, he and his father went to a baseball game. What role had baseball always played in their relationship?

5. What did Johnny learn about his father from the Marine manual in the third box?

Name ______________________________ Date ______________

Interpreting Analogies (page 641)

Building Vocabulary SkillBuilder

To complete an analogy, you first need to figure out the relationship between the capitalized words. There are various kinds of relationships that can be expressed. Some common types of analogies are shown here.

Common Types of Analogies		
Type	**Example**	**Relationship**
Part to Whole	SYLLABLE : WORD	is a part of
Synonyms	NICE : PLEASANT	means the same as
Antonyms	SICK : HEALTHY	means the opposite of
Cause to Effect	VIRUS : COLD	results in or leads to
Worker to Tool	WEAVER : LOOM	works with
Degree of Intensity	DISLIKE : HATRED	is less (or more) intense than
Grammar	ACCUSE : ACCUSATION	is grammatically related to
Item to Category	PAINTING : ARTWORK	is a type or example of

Complete each analogy. Then identify the relationship on which the analogy is based.

1. TEMPORARY : TEMPORARILY : : delicate : ______________ (delicious, delight, delicately, deliberately)
   Relationship: ______________
2. EAGLE : BIRD : : poodle : ______________ (dog, kitten, beagle, rooster)
   Relationship: ______________
3. SHEEP : FLOCK : : cattle : ______________ (herd, farm, fence, grass)
   Relationship: ______________
4. CONDUCTOR : TRAIN : : pilot : ______________ (flight attendant, plane, cockpit, wings)
   Relationship: ______________
5. JEOPARDIZE : SAVE : : abet : ______________ (assist, crime, help, prevent)
   Relationship: ______________
6. POLLUTE : CONTAMINATE : : extirpate : ______________ (emigrate, extirpation, uproot, deceased)
   Relationship: ______________
7. FRUGAL : CHEAP : : film : ______________ (allegory, words, pages, movie)
   Relationship: ______________
8. MISHAP : FIASCO : : sleep : ______________ (error, attention, hibernation, vigor)
   Relationship: ______________
9. SURGEON : SCALPEL : : carpenter : ______________ (hammer, clock, desk, wood)
   Relationship: ______________
10. HERETIC : BELIEVER : : insolence : ______________ (obedience, bucolic, dissension, polite)
    Relationship: ______________

Response to Literature

Prewriting

As you prepare to write your response to the literary work, fill in the chart below with basic information about the characters, plot, setting, and theme. Note specific lines and passages that had special meaning for you, and include the page or line numbers.

Characters
Plot
Setting
Theme
Passages

Response to Literature

Drafting and Elaboration

The passage below is from the first draft of a response to Edgar Allan Poe's short story "The Cask of Amontillado." Elaboration can make this paragraph more interesting and informative. Use the Suggestions for Elaboration, the information from the Reader's Notebook below, and your own ideas to add to the passage. Write your new paragraph on a separate sheet of paper.

Draft

On first reading, I thought it was great that Montresor gets away with the "perfect murder." He can wear a mask as he walks with Fortunato through the streets. That way no one can later say they saw them together the night Fortunato disappeared. The body will never be discovered, so it's the perfect crime. The body will never be found in the place under Montresor's house.

Suggestions for Elaboration

- Use precise, vivid language to make the paragraph more interesting.
- Be more specific in describing the personal response.
- Explain why no one will pay attention to Montresor wearing a mask.
- Include a quotation that describes the setting.
- Describe the place under Montresor's house.

Reader's Notebook

■ At first the writer admired Montresor's cunning. ■ The story takes place during "the supreme madness of the carnival season." ■ The streets through which Montresor and Fortunato walk are filled with revelers wearing masks. ■ Montresor takes Fortunato to catacombs beneath his house, supposedly to test the Amontillado wine. ■ The catacombs are damp, dark, and filled with human bones. ■ No one will hear Fortunato's cries for help in the catacombs or think to look for his body there.

Response to Literature

Peer Response Guide

Your response to a work of literature will be clear to you because you already know how and why it affected you. To find out if your response is as clear to your readers, ask a peer reviewer questions like the ones below.

1. How would you describe my overall response to this piece of literature?

   Response:

   Suggestions for Revision:

2. Where do I need additional quotations or references to the literature?

   Response:

   Suggestions for Revision:

3. What other points should I include to clarify my response?

   Response:

   Suggestions for Revision:

Peer Response Guide continued:

4. Which parts of my response, if any, are confusing or out of place?

Response:

Suggestions for Revision:

5. What questions do you have about the work or my response to it?

Response:

Suggestions for Revision:

6. Is the language of my essay appropriate to the subject and the audience?

Response:

Suggestions for Revision:

Response to Literature

Revising, Editing, and Proofreading

Revising

TARGET SKILL ▶ Using Active Voice

As you revise your personal response to a literary work, ask yourself the following questions:

- Have I used the active voice whenever possible, making sure the subject of the sentence performs the action?
- Does my introduction identify the work I'm writing about?
- Have I presented an interpretation of the literary work and shown how I arrived at it?
- Have I used quotations and examples to help explain my responses?

Editing and Proofreading

TARGET SKILL ▶ Misplaced Modifiers

Use the suggestions below to revise the following paragraph from a draft of a personal response to Poe's "The Cask of Amontillado." Then correct errors in grammar, usage, mechanics, and spelling with proofreading marks. Finally, copy your corrected draft on a clean sheet of paper.

- Correct any misplaced modifiers.
- Use the active voice whenever possible.
- Be sure pronouns have clear antecedents.
- Add a sentence or phrase that reflects a personal response to the literature.

Draft

For fifty years after the crime, I realized that Montresor has been alive. The crime has never been discovered. The body is still under his house. The crime was gotten away with but killing Fortunato didn't change anything. He has not been able to rest or live in peace, all because of his pride. That's what Poe implys, anyway.

Applying

Now edit and proofread your own response to a literary work. Refer to the bulleted list above.

Response to Literature

Strong Student Model

"The Cask of Amontillado"

1. Identifies the title, author, and main characters of the literary work; sets the scene and suggests the plot.

In his short story "The Cask of Amontillado," Edgar Allan Poe explores the theme of revenge. It's a story of a murder committed in a very unusual, even bizarre way. The setting is Italy in the 1800s during the celebration of carnival, a time of masquerade and wild partying. Montresor is the central character and narrator, a man who is angry with his acquaintance Fortunato because he believes Fortunato has insulted him. Montresor is a man of such pride that he considers an insult the ultimate wrong. He decides to avenge himself on Fortunato in such a way that his crime will go undetected and his victim will be fully aware of what is happening.

2. Tells enough about the story to make the personal response understandable.

He does this by preying upon Fortunato's pride. Well aware that Fortunato considers himself an expert on fine wines, Montresor claims he has bought a cask of Amontillado wine but tells Fortunato that he thinks he may have been cheated. Fortunato insists on sampling the wine and settling the question, especially when Montresor suggests that he might instead consult Luchesi, Fortunato's rival in wine expertise.

Luring Fortunato deep into the catacombs beneath the Montresor palace and plying him with wine, Montresor traps him in a tiny chamber among the dusty wine bottles and moldering bones. He chains the drunken Fortunato and then walls him up in this horrible place to die a slow death. Poe makes us realize that pride is the undoing of both men. I admired how Poe creates this mirror image of pride reflected in both murderer and victim.

3. Discussion of psychological subtlety of Poe's story holds the reader's attention and makes the writer's response more interesting.

4. Describes conflicting responses using specific details from the story.

Poe's story brought up some conflicting feelings in me as I read it, and especially as I thought about it later. First, I must admit, I felt some grudging admiration for Montresor's "perfect murder." Since it's carnival time, he can wear a mask as he leads Fortunato through the streets so that no one can later claim to have seen them together the night Fortunato disappeared. The body will never be discovered, so it's the perfect crime.

Then I began to feel some of the cold creepiness of the catacomb. I realized, going back over the story, that although Montresor says he has been wronged many times by this man, it is only an insult, a blow to his

Strong Student Model continued

pride, that drives him to murderous revenge. I saw that Montresor will always be trapped in his pride, as Fortunato is trapped in the catacomb, being painfully wounded by every passing insult.

Poe drives home this horror by the end of the story when we realize that fifty years later Montresor still lives and the crime has never been discovered. The last line gave me goosebumps, especially when I reread the story: *"In pace requiescat!"*—rest in peace. Montresor, Poe implies, has never been able to rest or live in peace because of his overwhelming pride.

5. Further explores the theme of the story, supporting the personal response with details and a quotation.

6. Explains how the story led to a personal reflection on how pride can lead to futile resentment.

I think I can safely say that I'd never be driven to murder out of pride or because of an insult. But how many times have I carried around the sting of an insult, reliving the pain long after I could have just let it go? Long after the person who insulted me had forgotten about it, I'd still be reacting, my pride forcing me to waste emotional energy. We see this in the story—long after Fortunato is dead, Montresor is still carrying the burden of his pride, his memory of the long-ago insult, and the guilt of being a murderer.

A few times when I've gotten some limited kind of "revenge" against someone, I felt good about it for a while, sometimes a very short while. But then I realized that my actions had left a bad taste. Montresor feels a hint of this in the story when he says, "My heart grew sick—on account of the dampness of the catacombs." We see that he will carry that dampness and ugliness deep in his soul.

The one place where we are all trapped, Poe seems to suggest, is in our own minds. What the story means to me is that just as Montresor chose pride and revenge, I am also free to choose. The image I think of when I look back on Poe's story is the dark, damp place of death as a symbol for the inside of Montresor's mind—no windows, no light, no freedom. I'm free to choose that kind of mind—or a place of confidence instead of pride, a place of forgiveness instead of revenge.

7. The writer concludes by describing some thoughts about the central symbol of the story and its personal significance.

Other Options:

- *Summarize the overall response to the story.*
- *Review how the response changed after reconsidering the story.*

Response to Literature

Average Student Model

"The Cask of Amontillado"

1. Identifies the title, author, and main characters; sets the scene and suggests the plot.

2. Uses too many short, simple sentences; sentence structure needs more variety throughout.

In his short story "The Cask of Amontillado," Edgar Allan Poe explores the theme of revenge. "The Cask of Amontillado" is the story of a murder committed in a very unusual, even bizarre way. It happens in Italy in the 1800s. It's the time of the celebration of carnival. This is a time of masquerade and wild partying. Montresor is the central character. He is the narrator, too. He is an angry man. He is angry with somebody he knows, Fortunato, because he believes he has been insulted by him. Montresor is a man with a lot of pride and he considers an insult the worst thing that anyone could do to him. He decides to get back at Fortunato in a way so that he won't be caught. And he wants Fortunato to know exactly what is happening to him when he gets back at him.

3. Tells enough of the story to make the personal response understandable.

Montresor knows that Fortunato boasts all the time about his knowledge of fine wines. He meets Fortunato on the street and tells him that he has bought some Amontillado wine. He tells Fortunato that he thinks he may have been cheated. Fortunato insists on trying the wine so he can tell Montresor if he's been cheated, especially when Montresor suggests he might go instead to Luchesi. (Luchesi is Fortunato's rival in expertise about good wines.) Montresor takes Fortunato deep into the catacombs beneath the Montresor palace, giving him a lot of wine to drink along the way. Fortunato gets pretty confused. Then Fortunato is trapped in a tiny chamber among the dusty wine bottles and moldering bones. He is walled up to die a slow death.

4. Draws a brief conclusion about the story's deeper meaning. This short paragraph could have been effectively combined with the paragraph below that begins "By the end of the story. . . ."

Pride is what ends up hurting both men. Montresor is driven by pride. Poe shows us that Fortunato is, too. I admired Poe's skill in showing them to be so similar to each other.

5. Repetitions here serve no rhetorical purpose.

I had some conflicting feelings in me as I read the story, especially as I thought about it later. First I admired Montresor for getting away with the "perfect murder." It's carnival time. That means he can wear a mask as he leads Fortunato through the streets. That means no one can later say they saw them together the night Fortunato disappeared. No one will ever find the body in the place under Montresor's house. That means the body will never be discovered, so it's the perfect crime.

Average Student Model continued

But then I began to feel creepy. I realized that although Montresor says he has been wronged many times by this man, it is only an insult, a blow to his pride, that drives him to murderous revenge. That's not worth killing anybody over. I saw that Montresor will always be trapped in his pride, just as Fortunato is trapped in the catacomb. Montresor will always be hurt whenever anyone insults him.

6. Uses evidence from the story to explain changing personal response.

By the end of the story I realized that Montresor has been alive for fifty years after the crime. The crime has never been discovered. The body is still under his house. He got away with it, but he has not been able to rest or live in peace, all because of his pride. That's what Poe implies, anyway. Killing Fortunato didn't change anything.

7. Clearly describes a specific personal response. Passive voice makes an awkward sentence.

Nobody would ever be physically hurt by me because they insulted me. However, there have been lots of times I felt bad after somebody insulted me, just feeling it over and over again. Sometimes when I got back at someone in some way I felt good about it for a while, sometimes a very short while. I could have just let it go, but I wouldn't. Even if the person who insulted me had forgotten about it, I was still reacting because of my pride. What a waste of energy! This happens in the story, too.

If I got back at somebody, I realized later that there was a bad taste in my mouth. Montresor feels this, too. He says "My heart grew sick—on account of the dampness of the catacombs." Probably that dampness and ugliness will keep being carried by him deep in his soul.

8. Uses quotation effectively to enlarge upon theme. Again, passive voice weakens last sentence in paragraph.

9. Misplaced modifier makes sentence unclear. Second sentence in paragraph seems to contradict the first.

In our own minds, Poe is saying we are all trapped. What the story means to me is that I can choose whatever I want—just like Montresor. The dark, damp place of death under the house can be seen as the symbol of Montresor's mind. That's the image that comes to me. There are no windows, no light, no freedom. I'm free to choose that kind of mind—or a better kind of mind if I want it.

10. Conclusion restates and develops the personal response.

Response to Literature

Weak Student Model

Poe's Story

In "The Cask of Amontillado," Poe explores the idea of revenge. "The Cask of Amontillado" is a story of a murder committed in a very unusual, even bizzare way. It happened in Italy in the 1800s. There was a carnival going on. Montresor is the central character. He is the narrator, too. He is an angry man. He is angry with somebody he knows, Fortunato, who he believes has insulted him. Montresor is a man with a lot of pride. An insult is the worse thing that anyone could do to him. He decides to get back at Fortunato. He doesn't want to be caught. And he wants Fortunato to know exactly what is happening to him when he gets back at him. He knows that Fortunato is always talking all the time about how much he knows about fine wines. Montresor meets Fortunato on the street. He says he has bought some Amontillado wine. He tells Fortunato that he thinks he may have been cheated. Fortunato insists on trying the wine so he can tell him if he's been cheated, especialy when Montresor suggests he might go instead to Luchesi. (Luchesi is Fortunato's rival in expertice about good wines.)

1. Identifies the title, author, and main characters; explains the setting and recounts the plot.

2. Misspellings and tense shifts weaken the essay throughout. The first paragraph is too long and rambling; it should be broken up.

3. Begins too many sentences with coordinating conjunctions.

4. The writer tells enough about the story to make the personal response understandable.

He takes Fortunato deep into the catacombs beneath the Montresor palace where he is supposed to taste the Amontillado. Fortunato is trapped in a tiny chamber among the dusty wine bottles and human bones. He dies a slow death after Montresor chains him to the wall and then walls him up in the chamber.

Pride is what ends up hurting both men. Montresor is motivated by pride. Fortunato is full of pride, too. That's why he never notices that Montresor hates him.

5. Suggests an interpretation of the story, but doesn't support it with examples and doesn't develop it.

I had some different kinds of feelings in me as I read the story, especially as I thought about it later. First I thought it was really neat that Montresor was getting away with the "perfect murder." He can wear a carnival mask as he walks with Fortunato through the streets. That way no one can later say they saw them together the night Fortunato disapeared. The body will never be discovered, so it's the perfect crime. The body will never be found in the place under Montresor's house.

6. Uses specific examples from the story to illustrate conflicting personal responses.

Weak Student Model continued

But then I began to feel creepy. Montresor was just insulted by the man, his pride is hurt. That's not worth killing anybody over. He overreacted. At least that's what I think. I saw that Montresor will always be hurt and angry whenever anyone insults him, always be trapped in his pride, just like Fortunato is trapped in the catacomb.

7. Explains personal response more fully. Run-on sentence should be corrected.

For fifty years after the crime, I realized that Montresor has been alive. The crime was never discovered. The body was still under his house. The crime was gotten away with, but he has not been able to rest or live in peace, all because of his pride. That's what Poe implys, anyway. Killing Fortunato didn't change anything.

8. Misplaced modifier and awkward use of the passive voice mar this paragraph.

I would never physically hurt anybody just because they insulted me. But there have been lots of times I felt bad after somebody insulted me. I just felt the insult over and over again. Sometimes when I got back at someone I felt good about it for a while, sometimes a very short while. I could have just let it go, but I wouldn't. Even if the person who insulted me had forgoten about it, I was still having a reaction because of my pride. What a waste of energy. This happens in the story, too.

9. Describes a specific insight as part of the personal response.

If I got back at somebody, I realized later that there was a bad taste in my mouth. Montresor feels this too.

10. Follows with a short, underdeveloped paragraph linking the insight to the story. Needs supporting quotation.

In our own minds, Poe is saying we are all trapped. But what the story means to me is that I can choose whatever I want. I can choose to nurse grudges, or I can choose to let bygones be bygones. Just like Montresor chose what he wanted. But then he had to live with it.

11. The writer's conclusion is weak. States vague thesis; relies on clichés; uses a misplaced modifier and a sentence fragment.

Other Options:
- *Summarize the overall response to the story.*
- *Review how the response changed after reconsidering the story.*
- *Use an image from the story to illustrate the thesis.*

Response to Literature

Rubric for Evaluation

Ideas and Content	Weak	Average	Strong
1. Includes an introduction that identifies the literary work and clearly states the writer's overall response to it			
2. Tells enough about the literary work so that readers can understand the response			
3. Contains clearly described, specific reactions and responses to the literary work			
4. Supports statements with quotations and details			

Structure and Form			
5. Uses language and details that are appropriate for the audience			
6. Uses well-organized paragraphs with good topic sentences			

Grammar, Usage, and Mechanics			
7. Uses the active voice			
8. Contains no more than two or three minor errors in spelling, capitalization, and punctuation			
9. Contains no more than two or three minor errors in grammar and usage			

Writing Progress to Date (Writing Portfolio)

The strongest aspect of this writing is ______________________________

____

The final version shows improvement over the rough draft in this way: ______________________________

____

A specific improvement over past assignments in your portfolio is ______________________________

____

A skill to work on in future assignments is ______________________________

Additional comments: ______________________________

____

from Black Boy

Richard Wright

Summary

Setting: Mississippi, 1923

In the eighth grade, Richard Wright is bored at school. One day he decides to write a story in class. The story is about a villain who wants a widow's home. Wright takes his story to the local Negro newspaper. The editor there publishes it. The editor also offers him a summer job as a local news writer. Wright thinks that his published story will win him some respect. However, the school has taught his classmates nothing about literature. They can't understand why anyone would write a story. At home, his grandmother calls the story a lie because it is made up. His mother worries that people will think he is "weak-minded." His uncle thinks the story is pointless. His aunt says using the word *Hell* in the title is sinful.

Wright dreams of moving to the North. There he could become a respected writer. He believes that everything is possible in the North. This belief keeps his dream alive. However, he says that the schools and segregation laws of the South are working against him. They are meant to stop black people from having goals and dreams. He wants a new way of life. However, that wish is dangerous because it is unknown.

Name ______________________________ Date ______________

from Black Boy (page 654)

Active Reading SkillBuilder

Making Inferences

Richard Wright, the author of *Black Boy,* does not directly state his opinion about the people he describes. Instead, he communicates indirectly through the choices he makes—choices about which events to recount, what methods of characterization to use, and how to structure the story. In order to understand the author's perspective toward these people, the reader must **make inferences** based on what is stated in the text and on common sense. As you read, complete the chart below by identifying three examples of dialogue and what they reveal about the person speaking. Then make an inference about the author's perspective on each person.

Character: Young Richard

What He/She Says	What This Reveals About Him/Her	Author's Perspective

Character: ______________________________

What He/She Says	What This Reveals About Him/Her	Author's Perspective

Character: ______________________________

What He/She Says	What This Reveals About Him/Her	Author's Perspective

Name ______________________ Date ______________

from Black Boy (page 654)

Literary Analysis SkillBuilder

Dialogue

Conversation between two or more characters in a work of literature is called **dialogue.** Well-written dialogue not only moves a story forward but helps the writer with characterization by revealing the personalities of the speakers. Reread one of the three primary dialogues in the excerpt from *Black Boy*—either one of the two conversations Richard has with the editor or the one he has with Granny. On the chart below, identify three or four passages from the dialogue and tell what each passage conveys about the character speaking.

Passage from Dialogue	Character Speaking	What It Conveys About the Character

Follow Up: Share your chart with other students. Discuss why readers might interpret the same passage of dialogue in different ways.

Name ____________________ Date ____________

from Black Boy (page 654)

Words to Know SkillBuilder

Words to Know

alien	hedge	intuitively	naive	speculate
articulate	heedless	mode	relent	stifle

A. Fill in each set of blanks with the correct word from the word list. The boxed letters will spell out what the editor offered in exchange for Wright's short story.

1. A good lecturer or master of ceremonies is this (and a *really* good one can tell jokes, too). ☐ _ _ _ ☐ _ _ _ _ _
2. If you don't really want to say yes but you don't really want to say no, you may do this. ☐ _ _ _ _
3. Something doesn't have to be from outer space to be this; it just has to be unfamiliar to you. ☐ _ _ _ ☐
4. Even with all their barometers and satellite photos, weather forecasters basically do this. _ _ _ ☐ _ _ _ _ ☐
5. If you feel something in your bones or know something you haven't been taught, this is how you know it. _ _ ☐ _ _ _ _ _ _ _ _
6. This can be a system, a procedure, a manner, a method, a process, a way, or a style. _ ☐ _ _
7. If this describes how you take care of your horse, you may find yourself steedless as well. _ _ _ _ ☐ _ _ _
8. You try to do this to your coughs if you're at a play and to your yawns if you're pretending to be interested. _ _ _ _ _ ☐
9. The phrase "a babe in the woods" describes a person who is this, since young children naturally are. _ ☐ _ _ _
10. You might beg, flatter, or plead in an attempt to get a stern person to do this. ☐ _ _ _ ☐ _

B. Write a short letter in which Granny or Aunt Addie expresses her worries about the narrator's writing activities. Use at least **four** of the Words to Know.

Name ______________________________ Date ______________________

from Black Boy (page 662)

Grammar SkillBuilder: Gerund Phrases

Key Concept: Writers use gerund phrases to provide a sense of ongoing action and to add variety to their sentence structures.

Gerund Phrases

A **gerund** is the *-ing* form of a verb used as a noun. A **gerund phrase** consists of a gerund, its modifiers, and its complements. Because it acts as a noun, a gerund phrase can be the subject of a sentence, a direct object, an object of a preposition, a predicate nominative, and an appositive. The examples below from *Black Boy* show two of these uses.

Object of Preposition: "Yet, by **imagining a place where everything was possible,** I kept hope alive in me."

Direct Object: "In me was shaping **a yearning for a kind of consciousness** . . ."

Activity

Rewrite each sentence, changing one of the elements to a gerund phrase. Underline the gerund phrase.

Example: Richard Wright read widely as a way to occupy his spare time.
Rewritten: Richard Wright occupied his spare time by reading widely.

1. I was looking for an outlet for my boredom, so I wrote a story.
2. It took me three days to compose that story of a villain who wanted a widow's home.
3. He pushed my writing to the side of his desk, which was tantamount to dismissing it and me.
4. The editor didn't seem interested enough to finish my story just then.
5. It did not seem fair to give my story to the newspaper for free.
6. The editor divided my story into three installments, which put my name before the public in an unexpected way.
7. My classmates could not understand why it was important to me to write a story.
8. In my school, literature was not taught as part of the curriculum.
9. I did something so inconceivable that it separated me from my classmates.
10. I did not want to get into an argument with my grandmother, so I evaded her questions.
11. I didn't realize that the controversy was really about the way I pushed the envelope of our proscribed existence.
12. I don't know where I got the idea that I should go north to accomplish my goals.
13. I had dreams that went against all that the educational system taught me I could be and do.
14. Mine were not dreams in which I amassed great wealth.
15. No one was there to warn me of the dangers ahead.

Name ______________________ Date ______________

from Black Boy (page 654)

Selection Quiz

Recall the events in Wright's short story. Then answer the questions in phrases or sentences.

1. Why did Richard Wright write his first story?

2. How did the newspaper editor encourage Wright in his writing?

3. Why were Wright's classmates unable to appreciate his story?

4. What was one example of his family's reaction to his story?

5. In what way was Wright "on the wrong track"?

Daughter of Invention

Julia Alvarez

Summary

Setting: New York City, around 1965

The narrator is a girl in the ninth grade. She has moved from the Dominican Republic to New York City. Her mother wants to be an inventor of useful gadgets. The narrator and her sisters laugh at her. Then one day the narrator's mother sees one of her ideas in the newspaper. Someone has stolen one of her ideas. She says that is proof that she is not crazy. She decides to be a serious inventor. However, no ideas come.

The narrator is chosen to give a speech for teacher's day. She is upset. She thinks her classmates will dislike her if she says nice things about the teachers. For weeks, she cannot write the speech. Finally, she happens to read a poem about individuality. She is inspired and writes her speech. Her father is shocked. He thinks it is disrespectful. He remembers living in the Dominican Republic. There talking about individuality could mean death. He tears up the speech. The narrator is upset. Her mother writes a speech for her. It is a polite speech. Later that day, the narrator's father brings her an electric typewriter. The speech was her mother's last invention. From then on, the mother lets her daughter do the "inventing" on her typewriter.

Name ________________ Date ________________

Daughter of Invention (page 663)

Active Reading SkillBuilder

Understanding Characterization

Writers can use four types of **characterization** to fully develop a character. They can (1) describe the character's physical appearance; (2) describe how the character speaks, thinks, feels and acts; (3) describe what others say, think or feel about the character; and (4) let the narrator make direct comments about the character. While reading "Daughter of Invention," notice how the author uses these techniques to bring the character of the mother to life. Write examples of characterization on the web below.

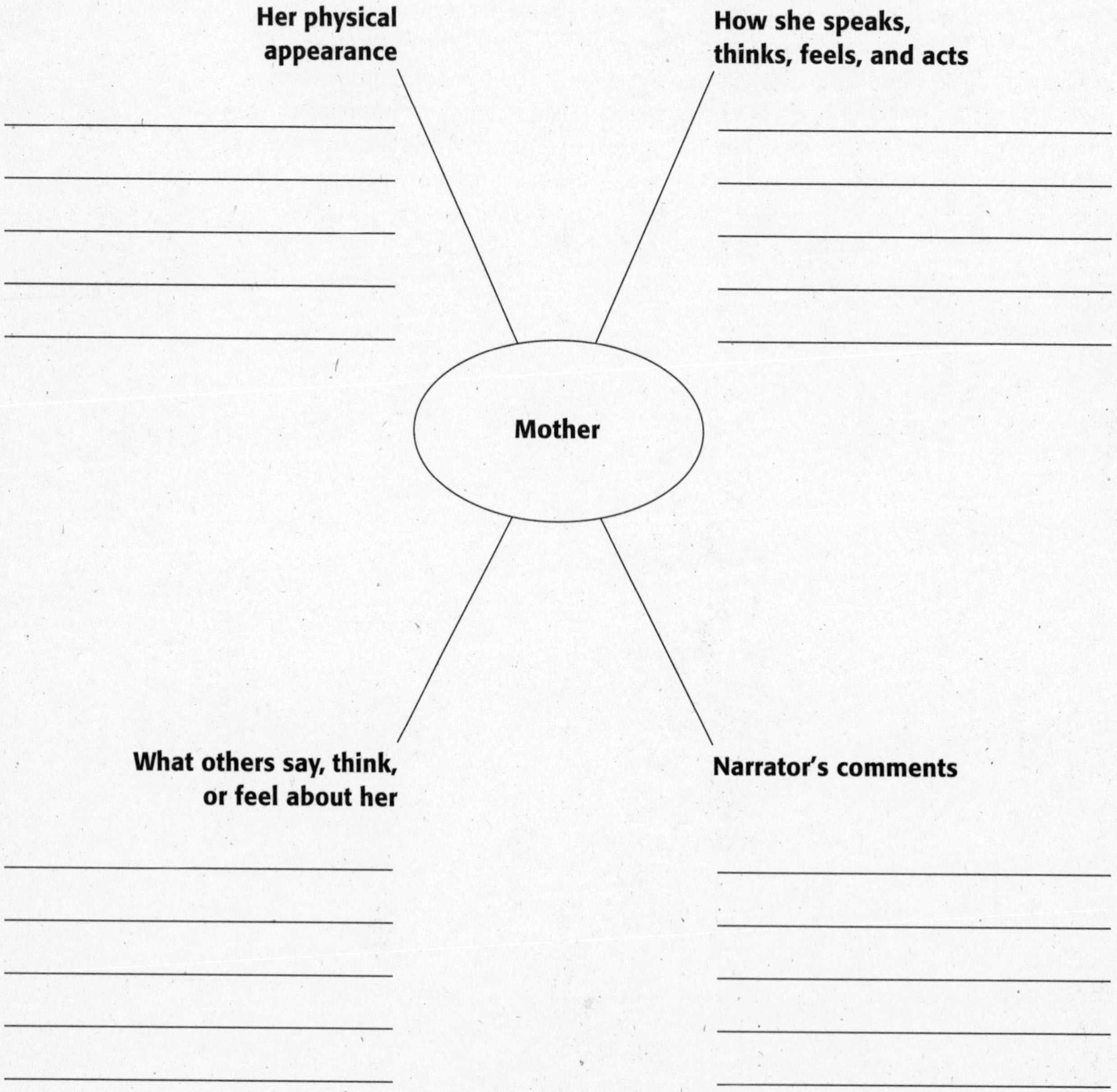

Her physical appearance

How she speaks, thinks, feels, and acts

Mother

What others say, think, or feel about her

Narrator's comments

Name ______________________ Date ______________

Daughter of Invention (page 663)

Literary Analysis SkillBuilder

Author's Perspective and Characterization

In fiction, what a character says and how he or she feels about an important issue will often provide clues to the **author's perspective.** A particular character may have strong opinions and attitudes, but the author may portray those attitudes in such a way that suggests his or her own viewpoint is very different. Reread "Daughter of Invention" and record clues in the characterizations that reveal Julia Alvarez's perspective on each issue in the chart. Based on these clues, write what her perspective on each issue is.

Issue	Clues in Characterizations	Author's Perspective
Life in the Dominican Republic		
Life in America		
Parent-Child Relationships		
The Role of Women		

Name ______________________ Date ______________________

Daughter of Invention (page 663)

Words to Know SkillBuilder

Words to Know

antibiotic	inhospitable	insubordinate	plagiarized	reconcile
idiom	innumerable	mortified	provoke	tentative

A. Circle the word in each group that means the same, or about the same, as the boldfaced word.

1. **inhospitable**	absent	disinterested	hostile	annoyed
2. **idiom**	word	expression	novel	introduction
3. **provoke**	irritate	attempt	prevent	restrict
4. **tentative**	reckless	uncertain	bold	unusual
5. **mortified**	unwilling	confused	resentful	ashamed
6. **antibiotic**	advertisement	advantage	drug	illness
7. **innumerable**	partial	countless	rewarding	uneven

B. Complete the following analogies by using the words from the word list. Remember that the second pair of words in an analogy should have the same relationship as the first pair. The colon in an analogy is read "is to," and the symbol : : is read "as."

1. PROBLEM : SOLUTION : : infection : ______________________
2. MONEY : STOLEN : : words: ______________________
3. TEAR : MEND : : separate : ______________________
4. CALM : ANGER : : soothe : ______________________
5. AGREEABLE : DISAGREEABLE : : obedient : ______________________
6. PLANETS : NINE : : snowflakes : ______________________
7. FRIENDLY : HOSTILE : : welcoming : ______________________
8. CAUTIOUS : RELUCTANT : : hesitant : ______________________

C. Think about the narrator's experiences in the story. Then write a short poem about a new and strange experience. Use at least **three** Words to Know in your poem.

Name ______________________________ Date ______________

Daughter of Invention (page 678)

Grammar SkillBuilder: Participial Phrases

Key Concept: Writers use participial phrases to add details and to vary their sentences. Because participial phrases are verb forms, they give a sense of action to writing.

Participial Phrases

A **participle** is a verb form used as an adjective to modify a noun or pronoun. A **participial phrase** consists of a participle and its modifiers. Participles have two forms: the **present participle** *(working)* and the **past participle** *(worked).* The past participle can be used with auxiliary verbs *(having worked).*

The sentence below includes both past and present participles. The first participial phrase modifies *newspaper;* the second and third modify *glasses.*

"On his side of the bed my father would be conked out for an hour already, his Spanish newspaper **draped over his chest,** his glasses **propped up on his bedside table, looking out eerily at the darkened room like a disembodied guard.**"

Activity

Combine each pair of sentences, changing one of them into a participial phrase. Underline the participial phrase.

Example: Julia Alvarez relates stories of her old life in the Dominican Republic. She has won awards for her writing.

Rewritten: Award-winning writer Julia Alvarez relates stories of her old life in the Dominican Republic.

1. My sisters and I battled with our parents. We were trying to become Americans.
2. Other students threatened us. My sisters and I decided we didn't want to go to school.
3. My mother sat on her side of the bed. She would make detailed drawings of her latest invention.
4. As my mother burst into my room, I cried out. I had lost the delicate strand of thought I was putting on paper.
5. I was annoyed by the interruption. I tried, nevertheless, to guess at her new invention.
6. Mami saw something unbelievable in the paper. She let out a yelp.
7. My father was startled awake by her cry. He thought immediately that they were not safe.
8. My mother pointed to the newspaper. She focused our attention on the suitcase with wheels.
9. Sister Mary Joseph asked me to deliver the teacher's day address at school. She thought she was doing me a favor.
10. Whitman's poems inspired me. I wrote the speech that enraged my father.

Name ______________________ Date ______________

Daughter of Invention (page 663)

Selection Quiz

Recall the events in Alvarez's short story and then answer the questions.

1. How does the discovery that someone has "stolen" her idea for suitcases with wheels affect the mother?

____

____

____

2. Why is the narrator at first unable to write a teacher's-day speech?

____

____

____

3. What ideas in Whitman's poetry finally inspire her to write a speech?

____

____

____

4. What memories of the Dominican Republic influence her father's opinion of the speech?

____

____

____

5. How is her mother's speech different from her own?

____

____

____

Name ______________________________ Date ______________________________

A Voice/The Journey (page 680)

Active Reading SkillBuilder

Understanding Diction

To gain a better understanding of a writer's use of **diction,** notice any words or phrases that strike you as vivid, unusual, or surprising, or that have strong associations with particular experiences, situations, or feelings you've encountered in your own life. As you read "A Voice," fill in the word webs below. Write an interesting word from the poem in the center of each web. Use the other circles in the web to explore the word's meanings and associations. One web has been partially completed.

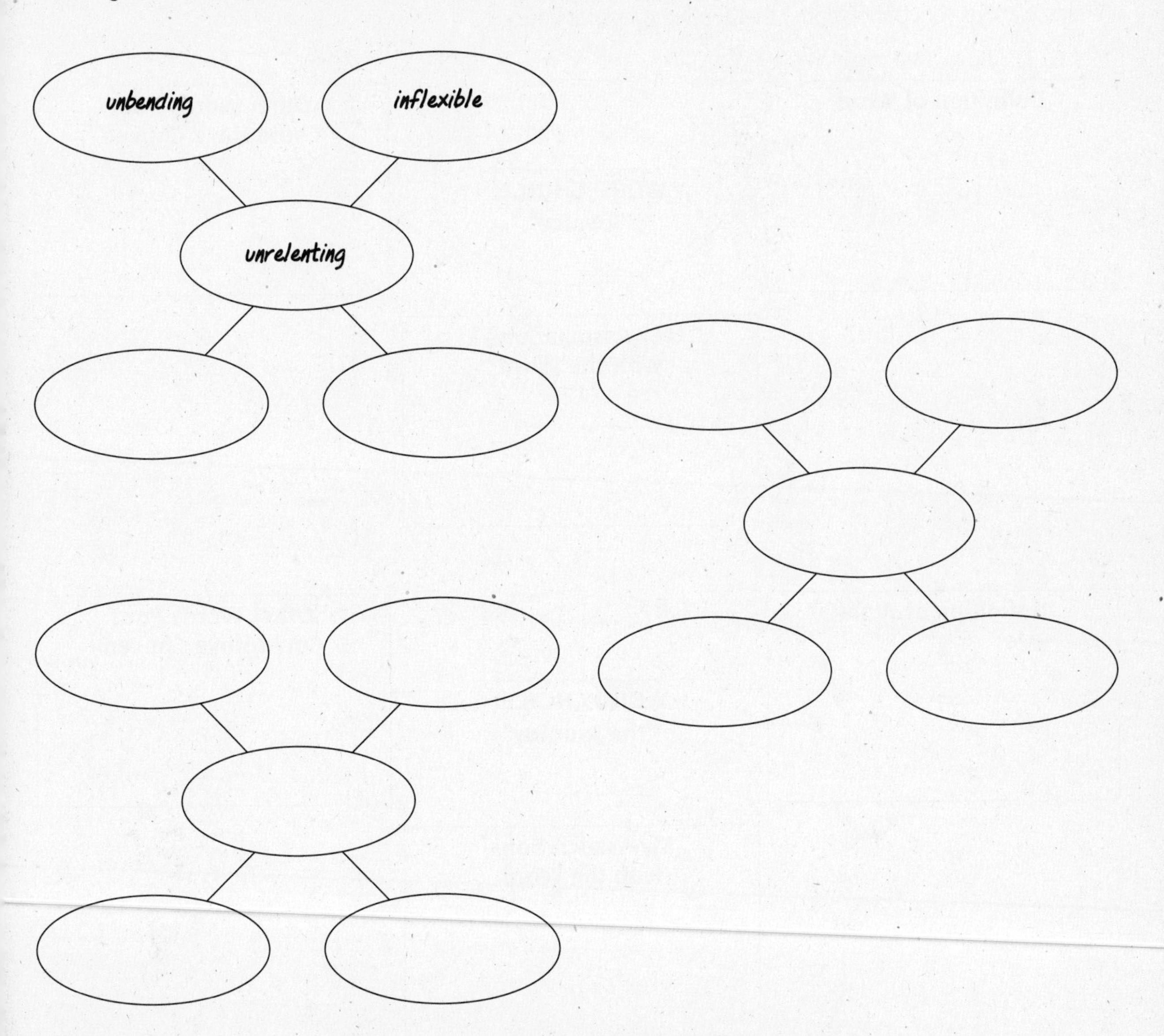

Follow Up: On a separate paper, make three more webs to fill in while reading "The Journey."

Name ______________________ Date ______________

A Voice/The Journey (page 680)

Literary Analysis SkillBuilder

Author's Perspective and Diction

An **author's perspective** is the viewpoint he or she expresses in a piece of literature. In poetry, this perspective is often disclosed, in part, through **diction.** Diction is a writer's specific choice of words and the way those words are arranged in a sentence. Reread "A Voice" and "The Journey," and select a word from each poem that seems to be particularly effective. Using the webs below, record the word, its definition or definitions, other words the poet could have chosen, and the associations (or connotations) that the word has for you.

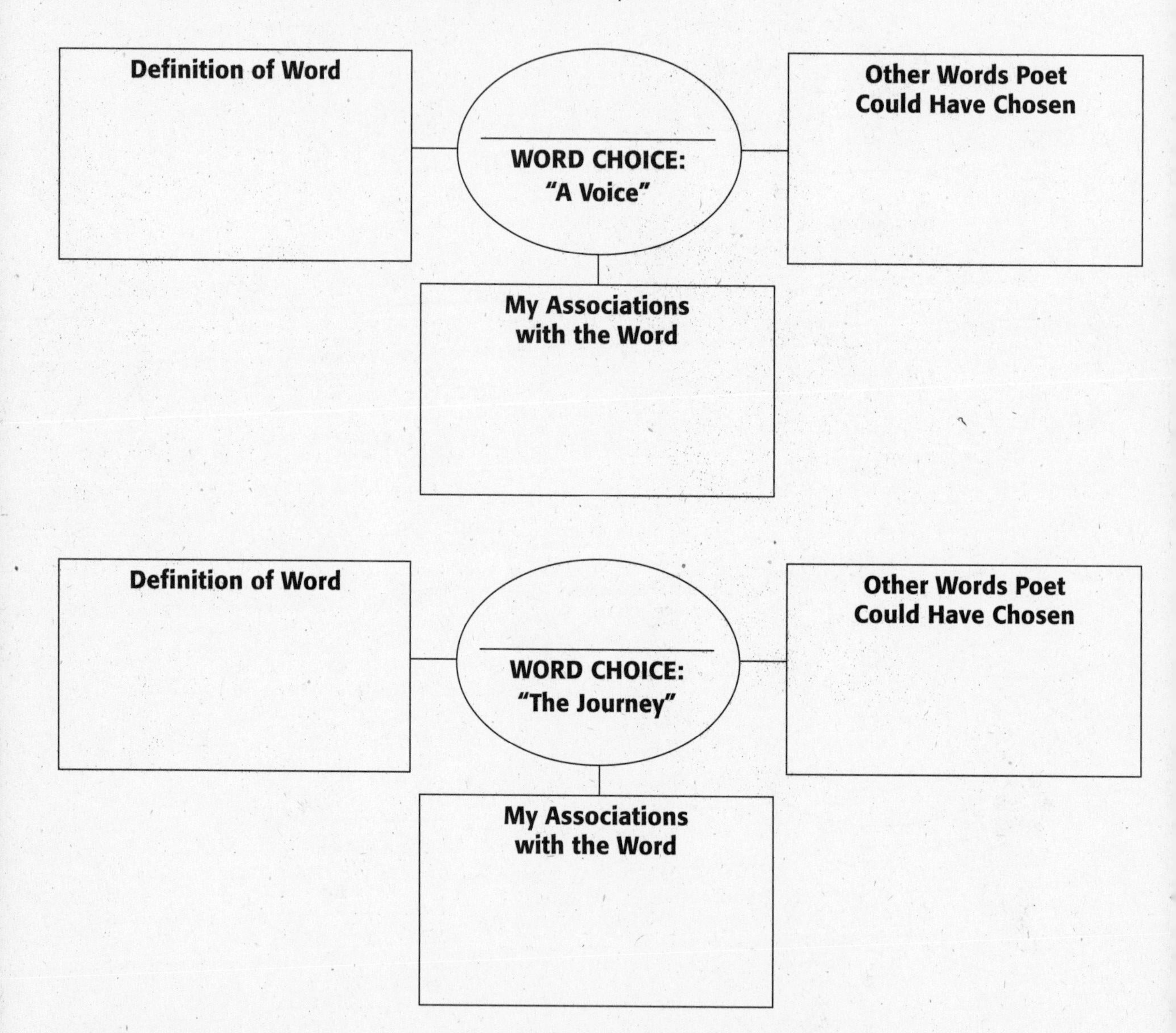

Follow Up: With a group of students, discuss what each word choice might reveal about the author's perspective.

Name ______________________ Date ______________

Denotation and Connotation (page 686)

Building Vocabulary SkillBuilder

Look at the words in each pair below. Think about the difference between the connotations of the words. Then write two sentences, each using one of the words. Be sure that the sentences reflect the connotations of the words.

1. aroma/smell ______________________
2. particular/picky ______________________
3. chat/chatter ______________________
4. train/educate ______________________
5. eternal/endless ______________________
6. imitate/mimic ______________________
7. childlike/childish ______________________
8. argument/debate ______________________
9. old-fashioned/outdated ______________________
10. leave/abandon ______________________
11. ashamed/embarrassed ______________________
12. control/dominate ______________________
13. excuse/forgive ______________________
14. unusual/peculiar ______________________
15. abundant/extravagant ______________________

Only Daughter

Sandra Cisneros

Summary

Setting: Mexico, United States 1960s–1980s

Sandra Cisneros is the only daughter in a Mexican-American family. She has six brothers. Her brothers will not play with her because she is a girl. So she has plenty of time to think, read, and imagine. Her father doesn't care what she learns in college. He only wants her to find a husband. So she is free to study English.

She wants to win her father's approval with her writing. But he cannot read English. He does not read fine literature either. Yet, he is the type of person she is writing about and writing for.

Her father likes to brag that he has seven sons. One of these "sons" is actually a daughter, Sandra. Sandra feels that she is being "erased" because she is a girl. She doesn't get married in college. So her father considers her education a waste. However, her writing career grows. She begins to make money at writing. One year, one of her stories is published in Spanish. At Christmas, she gives it to her father to read. He enjoys the familiar people and places in the story. He laughs at the humor. When he finishes reading, he asks her for copies of the story for their relatives.

Name ______________________ Date ______________________

Only Daughter (page 694)

Active Reading SkillBuilder

Understanding Generalizations

A **generalization** is a broad statement about a number of people or things. Valid generalizations are based on a wide range of evidence. Generalizations can be faulty if they are overgeneralized, lack the support of evidence, or contain the words *all, one, every,* or *never.* Generalizations are also faulty when they are stereotyped, or based on fixed, unfair ideas about all members of ethnic, racial, or other groups. As you read "Only Daughter," use the chart below to judge the accuracy of generalizations in the story about females and their roles. Write each generalization in the first column, then put a check in one of the other columns to classify it.

Generalization	Valid	Over-generalized	Stereotyped

Name ______________________ Date ______________

Only Daughter (page 694)

Literary Analysis SkillBuilder

Theme

A story's **theme** is the central idea or ideas the writer wishes to share with the reader. The idea may be a lesson that the story conveys about life or about people and their actions. Sometimes the theme of a work of literature is directly stated; at other times it is implied, and the reader must infer the theme. One way to interpret the theme is to think about what happens to the central characters. The importance of those events, stated in terms that apply to all human beings, is often the theme. In the chart below, write what you think is the theme of "Only Daughter." Then identify several passages in the essay that support that theme.

Theme:

Supporting Passages:

Name ______________________ Date ______________

Only Daughter (page 694)

Words to Know SkillBuilder

Words to Know

anthology embroider fulfill nostalgia trauma

A. Decide which word from the word list belongs in each numbered blank. Then write the word on the blank line on the right.

I wanted to fill up the tub and ran
The faucet so I could (1) this plan. ______________ (1)

The Thanksgiving dinner the year I was ten
Was better than any I've eaten since then,
And when I think back on that glorious meal,
I guess that (2)'s the feeling I feel. ______________ (2)

I gathered poems and stories about their search for mice,
Their scratching (very naughty) and their purring (very nice),
Their whiskers and their little feet, their harmonies and spats,
And published this (3) of writings about cats. ______________ (3)

She simply cannot tell the truth, so it is my prediction
That she'll (4) this event and change the facts to fiction. ______________ (4)
Although she only scratched her knee, I think the tale she'll tell
Will make it seem she suffered quite a (5) when she fell. ______________ (5)

B. Fill in each blank with the correct word from the word list.

1. An emergency room is also called a ______________ center.
2. Memories of childhood often produce ______________ if the childhood was a happy one.
3. How can you ______________ your dreams if you never open the door when opportunity knocks?
4. The author has chosen to ______________ the story of Shakespeare's life by inventing dialogues that never actually took place.
5. *A Child's Garden of Verses* is a famous ______________ of poems that appeal to the young and the young at heart.

C. Writers often dedicate their work to someone by saying something like, "For X, because . . ." Imagine that Cisneros had dedicated to her father the story she gave him to read. Write a few sentences that she might have used to compose that dedication. Use at least **two** of the Words to Know.

Name ______________________ Date ______________

Only Daughter (page 694)

Selection Quiz

Recall the events and ideas in Cisneros's personal essay. Then answer the questions in phrases or sentences.

1. When Cisneros was a young girl, how did her brothers' attitude toward girls help her to become a writer?

____

____

____

2. Once she was in college, how did her father's attitude toward women help her become a writer?

____

____

____

3. Aside from his general attitude toward women, what kept Cisneros's father from appreciating her writing?

____

____

____

4. Why did Cisneros's family move several times as she was growing up?

____

____

____

5. What did Cisneros think was the most wonderful thing that happened to her all year?

____

____

____

***from* The House on Mango Street**

Sandra Cisneros

Summary

Setting: Chicago, around 1970

Esperanza is a young girl growing up in Chicago. She and her family used to live in run-down apartments. They dream of owning a large, pleasant house, like the ones of TV. But the house they finally buy on Mango Street is small, ugly, and falling apart. Her parents say they will only live there for a while. Esperanza knows that they will stay.

Esperanza's name means "hope" in Spanish. To her it means sadness. She is named after her great-grandmother, a strong woman who never wanted to marry. She was forced later to marry. She spent her life looking sadly out the window. Esperanza does not want to take her great-grandmother's place by the window.

Esperanza's grandfather dies. Then she sees her brave father cry for the first time. She thinks about what she would do if he died. Then she puts her arms around him.

Esperanza's mother tells her, "I could have been somebody." She can speak two languages, sing an opera, and fix a TV. Now she just cooks and sews. She tells Esperanza to study hard so she can take care of herself. She says it is foolish for a woman to depend on a man.

Name ______________________ Date ______________________

from The House on Mango Street (page 701)

Active Reading SkillBuilder

Drawing Conclusions

When reading fiction, readers may have to **draw conclusions** about characters, events, setting, and other aspects of a story that have not been directly stated. To draw a conclusion, readers should notice details from the story, consider their own experiences and knowledge, and then make a logical guess about the meaning of the details in the story. As you read the excerpt from *The House on Mango Street*, draw conclusions about the three questions listed below. In the first column, write facts and details from the story that help answer each question. In the second column, list your own experiences or prior knowledge that relates to each question. In the third column, write your conclusions.

	Facts and Details from the Text	My Experiences and Prior Knowledge	Conclusion
How old is Esperanza?			
What past experiences has she had?			
What are her hopes and dreams?			

Name ____________________ Date ____________________

from The House on Mango Street (page 701)

Literary Analysis SkillBuilder

Vignette

The House on Mango Street consists of a series of 44 related vignettes. A **vignette** is a short, descriptive literary sketch that may stand alone or may be part of a larger work. Refer to the word web you created for Connect to Your Life on page 701. Then prepare to write a vignette either describing the physical features of your home or creating sketches of family members or people who live in your neighborhood. Identify your topic, then use the chart below to organize ideas and details about your topic.

Topic: ____________________

Ideas	Details

Follow Up: Use your notes to write your vignette.

Name ____________________ Date ____________

from **The House on Mango Street (page 709)**

Grammar SkillBuilder: Infinitive Phrases

Key Concept: Writers use infinitive phrases to be concise and rhythmic in describing the actions of characters or objects.

Infinitive Phrases

An **infinitive** is a verbal made from the word *to* and the base form of the verb. Infinitives can be used as nouns, adjectives, or adverbs in a sentence. An infinitive phrase consists of the infinitive, its complements, and its modifiers. The following examples from Sandra Cisneros's *The House on Mango Street* show some of the ways infinitive phrases may be used.

Noun as Direct Object: "I have inherited her name, but I don't want **to inherit her place by the window.**"

Adjective Modifying "turn": "Because I am the oldest, my father has told me first, and now it is my turn **to tell the others.**"

Adverb Modifying "gone": "They will not know I have gone away **to come back.**"

Activity

Rewrite each sentence, using an infinitive phrase to replace what is expressed by the underlined words. Underline the infinitive phrase.
Example: All of us wished that we each had our own bedroom.
Rewritten: All of us wished to have our own bedroom.

1. The family decided that it would leave one flat because the water pipes burst.

2. Before we went to bed, mother told us stories about the house that she hoped she would buy some day.

3. The nun from my school asked me if I would point out where I lived.

4. Mother likes it when she can combine doing housework with listening to opera records.

5. When you speak my name in Spanish, you make a soft, silvery kind of sound.

6. When my father told me of my grandfather's death, he started crying.

7. Mother decided that since she didn't have nice clothes, she would quit school.

8. My mother doesn't know which subway train will take her to the downtown area.

9. Writing all of my stories on paper helps the ghosts fade away.

10. Packing my bags, saying good-bye, and going away is what I want.

Name ____________________ Date ____________________

from The House on Mango Street (page 701)

Selection Quiz

Recall the events in Cisneros's vignettes, and then answer the questions in one or two sentences.

1. Why is Esperanza disappointed in the house on Mango Street?

2. What do Esperanza and her great-grandmother have in common?

3. Why did her great-grandmother spend her life looking out the window?

4. After he tells her that her *abuelito* has died, what does Esperanza do to comfort her father?

5. Why does Esperanza's mother want her to get an education?

On Writing *The House on Mango Street*

Sandra Cisneros

Summary

Setting: United States, early 1990s

The House on Mango Street grows out of Cisneros's own experiences. She begins writing it when she goes to graduate school in Iowa. There she feels very different from her classmates. She is afraid to speak in class. She thinks that she isn't as smart as her classmates. Then she realizes that none of the books she reads in school are about people like her. Cisneros is angry. She feels that her education has been a lie. It leaves out people from different backgrounds. She begins to write about the life that she knew as a child. She uses the kind of language that people used around her when she was a child. She has found her own "voice." She is proud of being different.

After graduate school, she works with Hispanic students. She begins to add stories from their lives to her book. Often she changes real events and people to make her ideas clearer. She writes from a young girl's point of view. That way, she can look at and overcome the shame she felt in her youth.

Cisneros didn't think she could help her people by writing. Yet, many readers tell her they share *The House on Mango Street* with their families. They tell her it is the story of their lives. This proves to her that her writing is of value.

Name ______________________ Date ______________

On Writing *The House on Mango Street* (page 711)

Active Reading SkillBuilder

Main Idea and Summarizing

The **main idea** of a work of nonfiction is the writer's most important, or central, idea. Sometimes the main idea is stated directly in a topic sentence, or it may be implied, or suggested, by the details the writer gives. To understand an implied main idea, the reader must make an inference based on the details.

A **summary** is a short restatement or retelling of written or spoken material. It includes only the main idea and the most important points and details. As you read "On Writing *The House on Mango Street,"* use the chart to list important details that relate to the topic of the essay. Then write the main idea of the essay in your own words, based on the details you have listed.

Topic: Writing *The House on Mango Street*

Important Details

Main Idea

Name ______________________________ Date ______________

On Writing *The House on Mango Street* (page 711)

Literary Analysis SkillBuilder

Voice

A writer's unique way of using language to convey his or her personality through writing is referred to as the writer's **voice.** Among the elements that work together to create voice are sentence structure, word choice, and tone. For example, some writers use short simple sentences, while others use long complicated ones. Certain writers use concrete words; other prefer abstract terms. A writer's tone, or attitude toward the subject, might be sarcastic, passionate, or humorous. Choose a passage from "On Writing *The House on Mango Street*" and analyze the sentence length, word choice, and tone. On the chart, quote examples from the passage that demonstrate these elements of voice and help to convey the personal, informal, and conversational voice that Cisneros uses.

Cisneros's Voice

Sentence Length	Word Choice	Tone

Follow Up: Now choose a passage by another writer from the unit. Create a chart like the one above, and analyze the voice in the passage. Describe how this other writer's voice differs from Cisneros's voice.

Name ______________________________ Date ______________

On Writing *The House on Mango Street* (page 711)

Words to Know SkillBuilder

Words to Know

affirmation evolve inception ingest presumption

A. Fill in each set of blanks with the correct word from the word list. The boxed letters will spell out the writer's way of using language to convey her personality in her writing.

1. This is what an idea can do: gradually develop into a full-blown story. _ [ ] _ _ _ _
2. Authors want this when they hope they have written a good story. _ _ _ _ _ _ _ _ _ [ ] _
3. Writers do this with books, as well as with lunch! [ ] _ _ _ _ _
4. This is the starting point for a story, poem, play, or biography. _ _ [ ] _ _ _ _ _ _
5. Writers make this when they assume that others will love their work! _ _ [ ] _ _ _ _ _ _ _ _

Complete the following sentence with the word that the boxed letters spell out.

Sandra Cisneros uses a ______________________ that is informal and personal in "On Writing *The House on Mango Street.*"

B. Think about each definition below. Then fill in the blank with the correct word from the word list.

1. ______________________: the act of assuming something is true
2. ______________________: to develop gradually
3. ______________________: something that supports the validity or truth of something else
4. ______________________: to take in, like food
5. ______________________: the beginning

C. Imagine that you are forming a Writer's Club. Write a list of guidelines for members to follow. Use at least **two** Words to Know in your guidelines.

Name ______________________________ Date ______________

On Writing *The House on Mango Street* (page 711)

Selection Quiz

Recall the events and ideas in Cisneros's essay. Then answer the questions in phrases or sentences.

1. When she first went to graduate school, why was Cisneros afraid to speak in class?

____

____

____

2. What suddenly made Cisneros angry about her education?

____

____

____

3. What did she do to rebel?

____

____

____

4. In *The House on Mango Street,* why did Cisneros write from the point of view of a young girl?

____

____

____

5. How does Cisneros feel that her writing has helped her community?

____

____

____

Character Sketch

Prewriting

To plan your character sketch, mentally review details about your character. Record these details in the boxes below. Then, decide on the main impression you want to give of the character, and write it in the space provided.

Appearance	
Actions	
Statements	
My Reactions	

Main Impression: ____________________

____

Character Sketch

Drafting and Elaboration

The paragraph below is from a draft of one student's character sketch. Revise the paragraph so that it includes more descriptive details. Use the Suggestions for Elaboration, the information from the Reader's Notebook below, and your own ideas. Write your revised paragraph on a separate sheet of paper.

Draft

The clothes he wears are like the costume of some guy from the fifties. The boots, the jeans, the leather jacket, the shades, the T-shirt, and the half-smile. It's like he walked right out of a fifties movie or an episode of *Happy Days* on TV. When he opens his mouth you expect him to have something cool to say or maybe to talk like the Fonz, but that's where his act breaks down: he sounds more like a whiny sixteen-year-old surfer.

Suggestions for Elaboration

- Elaborate on the kind of person upon whom the character models himself.
- Make the description more specific and vivid throughout.
- Rewrite the descriptive list so that it is a complete sentence.
- Mention specific movies from the 1950s.
- Indicate the kind of dialogue one might expect to hear from this character.
- Contrast the expected dialogue with his actual dialogue.

Reader's Notebook

■ His "uniform" belongs in the same world as James Dean and *West Side Story*. ■ His boots are Doc Martens, his jeans are black and cuffed, his jacket has more zippers than he knows what to do with, his T-shirt is white, and his sunglasses are mirrored. ■ He acts as though he walked out of *The Wild Ones* or *Rebel Without a Cause*. ■ You expect him to talk like the Fonz from *Happy Days,* putting his thumbs up and saying, "Aaaay!" or "You in Mr. M's class?" ■ "Math class is rough, dude," he said once at lunch; "Mr. Martinez is a real hard teacher."

Character Sketch

Peer Response Guide

You are familiar with the person who is the subject of your character sketch, but what impression of this person will the reader have? Will it be the one you hoped to give? To find out how effective your character sketch is, ask a fellow student to read your essay and answer the following questions.

1. How do you think I feel about this person?

   Response:

   Suggestions for Revision:

2. How would you describe the character's personality?

   Response:

   Suggestions for Revision:

3. What details help you to picture the character?

   Response:

   Suggestions for Revision:

Peer Response Guide continued

4. Can you think of any places where dialogue would bring the character more vividly to life?

   Response:

   Suggestions for Revision:

5. How does the setting help your understanding of the character?

   Response:

   Suggestions for Revision:

6. Do you feel that my character sketch has a strong conclusion?

   Response:

   Suggestions for Revision:

Character Sketch

Revising, Editing, and Proofreading

Revising

TARGET SKILL ▶ Word Choice

When revising your character sketch, ask yourself the following questions:

- Can I change some of my verbs to ones that are more specific?
- Are there places where I can add modifiers to describe how things look, smell, sound, taste, and feel?
- Can I include dialogue to help bring my character to life?
- Can I strengthen my conclusion by adding details and choosing more specific words?

Editing and Proofreading

TARGET SKILL ▶ Personal Pronouns

Refer to the bulleted list below to edit this paragraph from a student's first draft of a character sketch. Use proofreading marks to correct errors in grammar, usage, mechanics, and spelling. Copy your corrected draft on a separate sheet of paper.

- Check to see that pronouns agree with their antecedents in gender and number.
- Be sure that each pronoun is in the right case (nominative, objective, or possessive).
- Change verbs, as necessary, so they agree with their subjects.
- Fix any double negatives.

Draft

She walks purposefully across the airfeld to the small plane. My dad and me smile as we see passangers doing a doubletake. We know that everybody is rethinking their flying plans. But there isn't no other way to get around in this part of the Amazon. Besides, even at 78, my grandmother is one of the best pilots their are.

Applying

Now edit and proofread your own character sketch. Refer to the bulleted list above.

Character Sketch

Strong Student Model

"Call Me Elle"

We met in ninth grade AP English. She was a mid-semester transfer from a regular class. She strolled in dressed like she'd put on whatever was lying by her bed when she woke up that morning: tattered black leggings, a short gray skirt, a cardigan covered with cat hair, and a zippered leather jacket that was two sizes too big. Her hair was piled on her head as though she'd just bunched it up there and stuck in bobby pins until it stayed put. Yet despite her jumbled appearance, she seemed at ease with herself.

1. Captures reader's interest by presenting a vivid image of the character.

Parents are always telling us that it is important to make a good first impression. "Dress for success," they say, and a lot of kids at my school follow that advice. The guys wear slacks with sharp ironed creases, and the girls wear skirts and blazers, or even dresses. These students intend to get somewhere in life, and they use their clothes to show that they are serious about school. They believe that taking yourself seriously and taking your schoolwork seriously are the same thing. I should know. I was one of them, but I have learned otherwise.

2. Description of other students puts character's appearance in context.

Usually kids who dress like Ellen get teased by the other kids, but Ellen looked so comfortable and sure of herself that no one said anything. Somehow she seemed like a slumming supermodel, even though she didn't have the stunning good looks. The girls in class rolled their eyes, and the guys rolled their eyes too, but only after they'd checked her out. I thought to myself, "What a costume!" and assumed her brain would match her clothes: a grab-bag of thrown-together ideas and tattered notions she'd picked up here and there. I certainly didn't expect her to have any brains to speak of.

3. The writer focuses on character's appearance and mannerisms to show, rather than tell, what she is like.

Another Option
- *Tell what others say about the character.*

We were studying Shakespeare's sonnets that day. " 'Love is not love which alters when it alteration finds,' " Mr. Talmadge said. "Who can tell me what that means?" There was the usual silence after a tough question. You could have heard a pin drop.

But Ellen immediately spoke up, her voice measured and confident. "Isn't he saying that true love doesn't care about the little things?" She bit at the cuticle of one of her black-lacquered fingernails. "That love should not alter just because of, like, a change in appearance?" Mr. Talmadge,

4. Dialogue reveals another aspect of character that causes writer (and reader) to revise earlier assumptions.

Strong Student Model continued

excited to find a live student, had her explain the rest of the poem. As the weeks passed, it became clear that Ellen was quick—so quick that Mr. Talmadge stopped calling on her first because she always had the right answer. "Joyce's long sentences mimic how thought works," she'd say, surpassing us all. Or in another class, "*Romeo and Juliet* is so romantic *because* their love dies so soon. It's just all unfulfilled potential. If they had grown old together they'd probably be at each other's throats by forty."

5. Description of character's backpack hints, without saying directly, that she is studious.

After class she was always the first out the door, her stuffed-to-bursting backpack slung over her shoulder, her quick departures another part of her mystery. At lunch, people talked about her. One girl said, "She just thinks she's too cool." A guy added, "And those clothes! Where does she shop, Value Village?" A round of laughter followed. I laughed, too, though I wasn't sure why.

6. Shows typical behavior of people who dress like character.

Then one day at lunch I passed the table where she sits. I hadn't realized she was sitting there because the table was filled with a lot of people I don't associate with. They always look like they're going to a funeral or a punk rock concert and act as if school is for their entertainment. One of them, a bald punk named Laurie, called out, "Hey, preppie! Your skirt's wrinkled! You'll never get into college looking like that!" They all laughed. I just tucked my chin down and kept walking, until I heard Ellen yell, "Shut your mouth! There's nothing wrong with her. She's smarter than this whole table."

7. Character's comment reveals another side of her personality.

8. Strong, satisfying conclusion clearly demonstrates how writer feels about character.

I thanked her later. "Don't pay any attention to those kids," she said. "They can be a bunch of idiots. But you know what you're about." And then she stuck out her hand and said, "Call me Elle. It's what my friends call me." I have called her Elle ever since, as well as my friend—something I am proud to be able to say.

Character Sketch

Average Student Model

Elle

1. Description of character's appearance is intriguing, but would be improved by the use of vivid verbs and modifiers.

I first saw her in my ninth grade AP English class. She was a mid-semester transfer from a regular class. She walked in dressed like no one else in the class. She had on black leggings with runs, a gray skirt, a black cardigan, and a leather jacket. Her hair was in a sort of bun on top of her head, with pieces hanging out all over. It was surprising, though, that she didn't seem at all aware that her appearance was causing interest. In fact, she seemed totally relaxed.

2. Paragraph strays from description of character; connection to character is not made clear.

Parents are always telling us that it is important to make a good first impression. "Dress for success," they say, and a lot of us follow that advice. Guys wear nice slacks, and girls wear skirts and jackets or dresses. Kids like us intend to get somewhere in the world, and we use our clothes to show we take school seriously. Maybe it is silly, but that's the way we are. I guess it is practice for the business world, which is where I, at least, hope to end up. We know that clothes have a lot to do with how a person is perceived in a profession.

3. Writer reveals her response to character, but doesn't explain what it was about Ellen that kept her from getting teased.

Usually kids who dress like Ellen get teased by the other kids, but Ellen didn't get teased. The girls in class just rolled their eyes, and the guys rolled their eyes too, but only after they'd checked her out. I thought, "What a costume!" and figured her personality would be like her clothes: kind of scattered and weird. I wondered if she would survive in AP, since she didn't give the impression of being serious about school or anything.

We were studying Shakespeare's sonnets that day. " 'Love is not love which alters when it alteration finds,' " Mr. Talmadge said. "Who can tell me what that means?" There was the usual silence after a tough question while we all searched our brains.

4. Description of character's actions in class adds to reader's understanding of her, but use of dialogue would make description more vivid.

Then Ellen spoke up. She started talking about true love and about how appearance shouldn't matter. It was like she was explaining herself. As she talked, she bit at her black-lacquered fingernails. Mr. Talmadge looked pretty impressed and asked her to explain the rest of the poem. That was just the beginning. As the weeks went by, it became clear that Ellen was no dummy. It got so bad that Mr. Talmadge stopped calling on her first because she

Average Student Model continued

always had the answer. It was a little hard on the rest of us and didn't add to her popularity. First she came in dressed like that, and then she showed us up in class.

And then after every class she was first out the door, as though she didn't even want to try to be friends with any of us. Not that anyone wanted to be her friend. At lunch, one girl said, "She just thinks she's too cool." And a guy said, "And those clothes! Where does she shop, Value Village?" A round of laughter followed. I laughed with everyone else.

5. Dialogue is used to show that other students perceive character as thinking she is superior.

Then one day at lunch I passed the table where the outsiders sit. I didn't realize she was sitting there because I don't really look at those kids. They all act as if school is there for their entertainment. One of them, a bald punk named Laurie, called out some rude comment about my skirt. There was nothing wrong with my skirt but they all laughed anyway. I just kept walking, until I heard Ellen's voice say, "Shut your mouth. Clothes don't mean anything. She's smarter than this whole table." Maybe she's not so bad, I thought. I was pleased that she'd noticed me in class.

6. Use of Laurie's actual words would add to understanding of incident and contrast with Ellen's words.

7. With last statement, writer subtly shows that she actually admires character.

I thanked her later. She explained that all kids can be pretty mean and said that I shouldn't pay any attention to them. "You know what you're about," she said. Later she talked some more about judging people by their appearances, which I figured was a way for her to say that she knew what everyone in class thought of her. I felt bad about that. It was pretty nice for her to stick up for me.

8. Conclusion is weak and fails to convey that writer and character became good friends.

Character Sketch

Weak Student Model

New Girl in Class

1. Refers to character's appearance, but doesn't describe it, making it difficult for the reader to understand the writer's point.

My ninth grade AP English class is filled with the best students in the school. We all know each other and, I have to say, we all dress alike. One day we got a mid-semester transfer from a regular class. Ellen was dressed like you wouldn't believe. My friends and I all exchanged glances that seemed to say, Like who does she think she is? How people can dress like that and expect to be taken seriously? And she totally didn't fit in. But it didn't seem to bother her. And that was kind of surprising.

2. Begins too many sentences with conjunctions.

3. Tries to contrast Ellen's dress with writer's own clothes, but fails to describe the clothes.

Parents say it is important to make a good first impression. "Dress for success," they say, and all of us smart kids at school follow that advice. We dress like we would if we were working in an office or something, because wearing the right clothes puts you in the right frame of mind. Kids like us intend to go to college, and we use our clothes to show we take school seriously. People like Ellen dress like they don't care for things like getting an education. You can see why I might have thought little of her because of the way she was dressed.

4. Overuses word like, *which makes writing less interesting and too informal.*

5. Personal pronoun their *doesn't agree in number with its antecedent,* no one.

Kids who dress like Ellen get teased by the other kids, but Ellen looked kind of impressive and maybe a little scary. The kids in class rolled their eyes, but no one voiced their opinion out loud. I figured her personality would be like her clothes—sort of a mess. And I didn't expect her to take the class seriously or to be especially bright.

We were reading Shakespeare sonnets that day. " 'Love is not love which alters when it alteration finds,' " Mr. Talmadge read. "Who can tell me what that means?" There was the usual silence after a hard question as each student searched their brain.

6. Personal pronoun their *doesn't agree in number with its antecedent,* each.

7. Adding dialogue would make the events in this and the next two paragraphs come alive.

But then Ellen raised her hand. She started talking about true love and about how appearance shouldn't matter. It was like she was explaining herself. As she talked, she bit her fingernails. Mr. Talmadge liked what she said and asked her more about the poem. Over the next few weeks, it seemed like every time Mr. Talmadge asked a question her hand would go up. She was always right, too. In fact, Mr. Talmadge began to make a point of calling on the rest of us first to get us thinking as well. First she had to dress like that, and then she had to try to show us up in class.

Weak Student Model continued

After every class she was first out the door like she was running away from us, as though she didn't even want to try to be friends with any of us. Not that any of us wanted to be her friend. We pretty much looked at her as a pain in the neck. But somehow people were kind of interested in her, too, in a weird way. At lunch, people talked about her—her showing off and her clothes. Especially her clothes. And we resented that she thought she was better than us, or at least that's how we saw it.

8. Sentence fragment should be rewritten as a complete sentence.

Then one day at lunch I walked past the table where the outsiders sit. I didn't even see her, not that I really look at those kids. They all act as if school is there for their entertainment. They dress like they're going to their own funeral. One of them, a bald punk named Laurie, called out some rude, obviously jealous comment about my skirt. There was nothing wrong with my skirt but they all laughed anyway. I just kept walking, and then I heard Ellen's voice telling them to shut up. She went on to say that I was smarter than anyone at the table.

I thanked her later. She said those kids can be pretty mean, and that I shouldn't listen to them. Then she said more about judging people by their appearance, which I figured was a way for her to say that she knew what we had all been thinking about her. She smiled and stuck out her hand and told me to call her "Elle." What could I do but shake her hand?

9. Weak conclusion doesn't resolve the relationship between the writer and the character, Ellen.

Character Sketch

Rubric for Evaluation

Ideas and Content	**Weak**	**Average**	**Strong**
1. Presents a vivid picture of the personality and physical appearance of a person			
2. Establishes a dominant, or main, impression of the person			
3. Reveals the writer's response to the person			
4. Places the character in a context that contributes to the reader's understanding of the character			

Structure and Form			
5. Includes dialogue, mannerisms, descriptions, and other devices that show rather than tell what the character is like			
6. Has a clear organizational structure and a strong conclusion			
7. Uses specific verbs and modifiers to describe how things look, smell, sound, taste, and feel			

Grammar, Usage, and Mechanics			
8. Contains no more than three minor errors in grammar and usage			
9. Contains no more than three minor errors in spelling, capitalization, and punctuation			

Writing Progress to Date (Writing Portfolio)

The strongest aspect of this writing is ______________________________

____

The final version shows improvement over the rough draft in this way: ______________________________

____

A specific improvement over past assignments in your portfolio is ______________________________

____

A skill to work on in future assignments is ______________________________

Additional comments: ______________________________

____

Reflecting on Theme (page 726)

Reflect and Assess

OPTION 3 **Evaluating Writing About the Family**

Anthology Title: ______________________________

Selections to Be Included (in order):

____

____

____

____

____

Introduction

Answer Key
Unit Four

The Scarlet Ibis

Active Reading SkillBuilder, page 5

(Students' responses will vary. Sample responses are provided.)

Passage: "I began to make plans to kill him by smothering him with a pillow."

Inference: The narrator is without empathy and sympathy for his brother and is irrational in his thinking.

Passage: "Renaming my brother was perhaps the kindest thing I ever did for him, because nobody expects much from someone called Doodle."

Inference: The narrator expects little from his brother and has doomed him to a life of low expectations from others.

Passage: One day I took him up to the barn loft and showed him his casket, telling him how we all had believed he would die.

Inference: The narrator can be cruel.

Conclusion: The older brother, who is still a child himself, feels wronged by what he considers to be the misfortune of not having a "normal" sibling. He practices seemingly uncontrollable acts of cruelty toward him.

The Scarlet Ibis

Literary Analysis SkillBuilder, page 6

(Students' responses will vary. Sample responses are provided.)

What Narrator Learns

- Doodle really is a companion, someone with whom he can share the place he loves, Old Woman Swamp.
- People can sometimes be very cruel to those they love, especially those who are their own flesh and blood.
- Pride can cause either life or death.
- The narrator loved his fragile, sensitive brother.

Key Passages

- "Doodle was my brother, and he was going to cling to me forever, no matter what I did, so I dragged him across the burning cotton field to share with him the only beauty I knew, Old Woman Swamp."
- "There is within me (and with sadness I have watched it in others) a knot of cruelty borne by the stream of love, much as our blood sometimes bears the seed of our destruction, and at times I was mean to Doodle."
- "But all of us must have something or someone to be proud of, and Doodle had become mine. I did not know then that pride is a wonderful, terrible thing, a seed that bears two vines, life and death."
- "For a long, long time, it seemed forever, I lay there crying, sheltering my fallen scarlet ibis from the heresy of rain."

Importance of Title

- The scarlet ibis, like the beauty of Old Woman Swamp and like Doodle's fragile goodness, is rare and "beyond the touch of the everyday world."
- The scarlet ibis's red color symbolizes life-giving blood, the blood that runs through families that can sometimes carry "the seed of our destruction." It also symbolizes loss of life: the blood that stains Doodle's shirt, Doodle's death under the red nightshade bush, and the bird's death under the bleeding tree.
- The scarlet ibis symbolizes both life and death, beauty and sadness.
- The narrator calls Doodle his scarlet ibis. He realizes too late that like the ibis, Doodle was tired and fragile and needed protection from the harshness of life.

Follow Up: Students' sentences will vary, but should show an understanding of the themes in the selection.

The Scarlet Ibis

Words to Know SkillBuilder, page 7

A.
1. reiterate
2. careen
3. imminent
4. heresy
5. iridescent
6. doggedness

B.
1. infallibility
2. exotic
3. invalid
4. precariously

C. Students' advice will vary. Accept responses that accurately use at least three Words to Know.

Grammar SkillBuilder

Prepositional Phrases, page 8

(Answers will vary.)

1. Until he learned to crawl, Doodle stayed on the rubber sheet on the bed.
2. Daddy built Doodle a go-cart, and I carted him around the piazza.
3. I dragged poor Doodle in his go-cart to Old Woman Swamp.
4. One day I took Doodle into the barn loft and made him touch the coffin with his trembling fingers.
5. When I first started to teach him to walk, he fell each time like a half-empty sack.
6. We surprised the family when Doodle walked across the dining room and sat in his chair.

7. He had practiced walking every day that summer in Old Woman Swamp.
8. That summer many trees in our yard were uprooted by a hurricane.
9. The beautiful dying bird with the scarlet feathers must have been blown in by the hurricane.
10. I ran toward home in the rain, and when I went back I found Doodle had fallen beside the road.

The Scarlet Ibis
Selection Quiz, page 9

1. He had wanted a companion he could run, box, and climb trees with. Doodle will always be too weak to do these things.
2. He cries because the swamp is so beautiful.
3. He seems very sad, and he buries the bird in a flower garden.
4. It has become clear that Doodle won't meet the goals he has set for him, and he is angry.
5. Doodle and the bird look similar in death. Like the bird, Doodle is thin and fragile. His neck and shirt are red with blood.

Lineage/The Courage That My Mother Had
Active Reading SkillBuilder, page 10
(Students' answers will vary. Sample responses are provided.)
Lineage
Speaker's Values: respects her ancestors; honors the role of women; intrigued with the past
Speaker's Feelings: admiration; love
Speaker's Sense of Identity: insecure; does not feel she possesses the strength of her grandmothers, nor is she secure in having contributed as her grandmothers did
The Courage That My Mother Had
Speaker's Values: loves and honors her mother; values her courage; treasures her mother's belongings, but even more so her mother's gift of courage
Speaker's Feelings: love; admiration; reverence
Speaker's Sense of Identity: vulnerable; longs for the courage that her mother had and that she feels she does not possess

Lineage/The Courage That My Mother Had
Literary Analysis SkillBuilder, page 11
(Sample responses are given.)
Alliteration: strong, sturdiness, singing; sowing seed; grain grew; smelling, soap; followed, field, full; rolling roughly; quarried, granite; wore, wear; thing, that; something, spare
Repetition: My grandmothers were strong (three times); full of/full of; with her/with her; granite/granite; courage/courage; my mother/my mother
Assonance: moved, through; sowing, followed, rolling; Rock, quarried; went, left, instead
Follow Up: In "Lineage," the first and last lines end with the word "strong." This and other repeated sounds give a sense of strength, motion, and hard work. In "The Courage That My Mother Had," the sound devices help describe the rock-solid character of the mother and her "courage like a rock."

My Papa's Waltz/Grape Sherbet
Active Reading SkillBuilder, page 12
(Students' responses will vary. Sample responses are provided.)
My Papa's Waltz: whiskey on your breath; romped until the pans slid; battered hand; ear scraped a buckle; beat time on my head; palm caked hard by dirt; clinging to your shirt
Grape Sherbet: swirled snow, gelled light; cheering; cap turned up so the bib resembles a duck; galloped through the grassed-over mounds; dollop of sherbet; salt on a melon that makes it sweeter; grandmother stares from the porch

My Papa's Waltz/Grape Sherbet
Literary Analysis SkillBuilder, page 13
(Students' responses will vary. Sample responses are provided.)
Images in "My Papa's Waltz"
Sight: still clinging to your shirt
Hearing: romped until the pans fell from the kitchen shelf
Smell: whiskey on your breath
Touch: hand that held my wrist; my right ear scraped a buckle; beat on my head
Images in "Grape Sherbet"
Sight: swirled snow, gelled light; cap turned up so the bib resembles a duck; grandmother stares from the porch
Hearing: galloped through the grassed-over mounds
Taste: like salt on a melon that makes it sweeter; how we imagined lavender would taste
Follow Up: Students' memories, sketches, and poems will vary. Check for an understanding of the use of sensory details and imagery to help readers experience the topic of the poem.

Marine Corps Issue
Active Reading SkillBuilder, page 15
(Responses will vary. Sample responses are provided.)
Effects of the Vietnam War
On the Father
". . . my father had damaged hands—a degenerative arthritis, we were told . . . large, leprous hands, thick with scar tissue and slightly curled."

"Even after my father's return tension and distance continued for some time."
"A visitor would have no idea about my father's military career were it not evident in his walk and demeanor."
". . . he'd been wounded in some unknown place . . . his friends had been killed, and his sons had grown without him."

On the Family

". . . for the first ten months of my life . . . I had no father . . . that is, he had never seen me."
"My mother's life intrigues me . . . She has never spoken about that time, not even about the four continuous years of my father's absence, when . . . she would spend at least two hours every night weeping alone . . ."
"Our family was different from others. . . . We had no open animosity toward each other, only distance."
"My summer project would be to learn about the war and my father's place there."
". . . baseball. It had always been the bridge between us. There had always been the gap and one bridge, a love of the game."

Marine Corps Issue

Literary Analysis SkillBuilder, page 16
(Responses will vary. Sample responses are provided.)
Flashback: At the age of five, Johnny jumps out at his father and shouts "Boo!" His father attacks him.
What Johnny Learns About His Father: His father becomes violent when startled.
Flashback: Johnny sees the movie *Apocalypse Now.*
What Johnny Learns About His Father: He gains his first impressions of what his father experienced during the war.
Flashback: Johnny's mother begs him not to ask his father "to start remembering again."
What Johnny Learns About His Father: Johnny learns that his father's memories of the war are very painful.
Flashback: Johnny reads the pamphlet titled *Escape and Torture.*
What Johnny Learns About His Father: He learns that his father was tortured.

Marine Corps Issue

Words to Know SkillBuilder, page 17

A.
1. grotesque
2. devoid
3. demeanor
4. disjunction
5. deprivation
6. agitated
7. vulnerability
8. intrigue
9. trepidation
10. animosity

B. Students' paragraphs will vary. Accept responses that accurately use at least four Words to Know.

Grammar SkillBuilder

Appositive Phrases, page 18
(Answers will vary.)

1. The first time I saw what was in the boxes was when Dad's friend, a man he knew from his days as a Marine, came to visit.
2. The film *Apocalypse Now* opened Johnny's eyes to his father's history.
3. After seeing the film, Johnny went to the library and borrowed three books, each one about the Vietnam War.
4. His summer project was to learn about the Vietnam War, his father's war.
5. Johnny went to his sanctuary, a quiet spot at the back of the garden, to read each day.
6. His mother begged Johnny not to make Dad think about his memories, memories that were long buried.
7. One day during that summer of drought, my brother, Joe, and I drove by a withered cornfield.
8. I showed Joe *Great Expectations* and *Dispatches,* the two books I bought.
9. The locks, common hardware store padlocks, must have come with two keys.
10. The top tray contained family memorabilia, report cards and assorted photographs.
11. In his platoon book, the one dated 1964, San Diego, Johnny found pictures of a younger, less tired version of his father.
12. Johnny's namesake, Jonathan Allen Whitney, was also pictured in the book.
13. One of the photos in the second box, a hideous picture of a newborn Johnny, had an inscription on the back.
14. Father and son went to the Cardinals game, a game that went twelve innings.
15. Johnny's father, a man he loved and respected, only spoke of the war in brief, slow monologues.

Marine Corps Issue

Selection Quiz, page 19

1. During the Vietnam War, the name Charlie was a slang term for the enemy. Because the name had a negative meaning for his father, Johnny was renamed after an American soldier who had died.
2. Because of his war experience, his father reacted violently to being startled. When Johnny startled his father by jumping out at him and saying "Boo!" his father struck him.

3. His father never talked about the war. His mother asked him not to discuss the war with his father because it had taken his father so long to forget his experiences.
4. Baseball was the one thing that they could share and talk about. It made them feel close to each other.
5. He learned that his father's crippled hands and scarred leg were the result of being tortured as a prisoner of war.

Building Vocabulary SkillBuilder
Interpreting Analogies, page 20

1. delicately; is grammatically related to
2. dog; is a type or example of
3. herd; is a part of
4. plane; works with
5. prevent; means the opposite of
6. uproot; means the same as
7. movie; means the same as
8. hibernation; is less intense than
9. hammer; works with
10. obedience; means the opposite of

***from* Black Boy**
Active Reading SkillBuilder, page 34
(Responses will vary. Sample responses are provided.)
Character: Young Richard
What He Says: "But you're asking me to *give* you my story, but you don't *give* your papers away."
What This Reveals About Him: He is logical, self-assured, determined, and wary of being taken advantage of.
Author's Perspective: Wright is amused at and proud of his boldness and determination as a young boy.
Character: the editor
What He Says: "Then come and see me before you take another job . . . And write some more stories."
What This Reveals About Him: He acknowledges the boy's talent, is understanding of his attitude, and wants to encourage him in any way he can.
Author's Perspective: He appreciates the editor's role in launching his writing career.
Character: Granny
What She Says: "Then it's a lie."
What This Reveals About Her: She is uninformed and rigidly narrow in her thinking.
Author's Perspective: His grandmother was typical of the kind of person he needed to escape in order to fulfill himself.

***from* Black Boy**
Literary Analysis SkillBuilder, page 35
(Responses will vary. Sample responses are provided.)
Passage from Dialogue: "But you sell your papers for money."
Character Speaking: Richard
What It Conveys About the Character: He is confident, assertive, intelligent, and logical.
Passage from Dialogue: "But if the story is good enough to sell to your readers, then you ought to give me some of the money you get from it."
Character Speaking: Richard
What It Conveys About the Character: He does not give up easily; he won't let anyone take advantage of him.
Passage from Dialogue: "I'm going to offer you something more valuable than money . . . I'll give you a chance to learn to write."
Character Speaking: the editor
What It Conveys About the Character: He is patient and kind; he sees Richard's potential; he wants to give him an opportunity.
Passage from Dialogue: "I work mornings and evenings for three dollars a week."
Character Speaking: Richard
What It Conveys About the Character: He is hard-working and responsible.
Follow Up: Responses will vary. Students may recognize that differences in readers' personal backgrounds, values, and experiences might cause them to interpret dialogue differently.

***from* Black Boy**
Words to Know SkillBuilder, page 36

A.
1. articulate
2. hedge
3. alien
4. speculate
5. intuitively
6. mode
7. heedless
8. stifle
9. naive
10. relent

The boxed letters spell out a chance to learn.
B. Students' letters will vary. Accept responses that accurately use at least four Words to Know.

Grammar SkillBuilder
Gerund Phrases, page 37
(Answers will vary.)

1. I found an outlet for my boredom by writing a story.
2. Composing that story of a villain who wanted a widow's home took me three days.
3. His pushing my writing to the side of his desk was tantamount to dismissing it and me.
4. The editor didn't seem interested in finishing my story just then.

5. Giving my story to the newspaper for free did not seem fair.
6. By dividing my story into three installments, the editor put my name before the public in an unexpected way.
7. My classmates could not understand why writing a story was important to me.
8. In my school, the teaching of literature was not part of the curriculum.
9. Doing something so inconceivable separated me from my classmates.
10. Instead of getting into an argument with my grandmother, I evaded her questions.
11. I didn't realize that the controversy was really about my pushing the envelope of our proscribed existence.
12. I don't know where I got the idea of going north to accomplish my goals.
13. My dreaming went against all that the educational system taught me I could be and do.
14. Mine were not dreams of amassing great wealth.
15. No one was there with warnings of the dangers ahead.

from Black Boy
Selection Quiz, page 38

1. He was bored in class and wrote the story to entertain himself.
2. He published Wright's story and offered him a summer job writing for the paper.
3. His classmates had never been taught anything about literature.
4. One possible answer is, his grandmother called it a lie because it was fiction.
5. He was on the wrong track because he dreamed of becoming a respected writer, and he wanted to do the very things society told him were impossible for him to achieve.

Daughter of Invention
Active Reading SkillBuilder, page 40
(Responses will vary. Sample responses are provided.)
Her physical appearance: her eyes would widen with worry; her reading glasses would ride the bridge of her nose; she listened attentively; her face was soft and warm and proud
How she speaks, thinks, feels, and acts: says "When in Rome, do unto the Romans . . ."; likes to read *The New York Times;* wags her finger; laughs eerie laughs like "crazy people in movies"; feels proud of her daughter's accomplishments in school; defends her daughter against her father's anger
What others say, think, or feel about her: all of the daughters resented the mother's preoccupation with gadgets; her husband is furious when she joins forces with their daughter against him
Narrator's comments: says "she was a good enough Mamie, fussing and scolding and giving advice," but she thinks her mother doesn't want the girls to become Americans; she is like some devoted scholar; she is proof of the *perpetuum mobile* machine; "I could tell, though, by the look on her face, it was as if one of those stones the kids had aimed at us had hit her."

Daughter of Invention
Literary Analysis SkillBuilder, page 41
(Students' responses may vary. Sample responses are provided.)
Issue: Life in the Dominican Republic
Clues in Characterizations: "There was terror in his voice, fear she'd seen in his eyes in the Dominican Republic before we left. We were being watched there; he was being followed; he and Mother had often exchanged those looks."
Author's Perspective: Life was frightening in the Dominican Republic, and Father still harbored that fear.
Issue: Life in America
Clues in Characterizations: "Here, we were trying to fit in America among Americans; we needed help figuring out who we were, why these Irish kids whose grandparents were micks two generations ago, why they were calling us spics."
Author's Perspective: She is resentful and upset that the Irish, who were not so long ago the new immigrants to America, are now the ones who call her names.
Issue: Parent-Child Relationships
Clues in Characterizations: ". . . here was our own mother, who didn't have a second to help us puzzle any of this out, inventing gadgets to make life easier for American moms . . . arming our own enemy against us!"
Author's Perspective: The author is confused about how to handle growing up in a different country; she resents her mother's preoccupation with inventing gadgets.
Issue: The Role of Women
Clues in Characterizations: "She did not want to go back to the old country where she was only a wife and mother (and a failed one at that, since she had never had the required son)."
Author's Perspective: She believes it is wrong that women in the Dominican Republic are valued only for their ability to bear sons because it implies that girls are not as desirable.

Daughter of Invention
Words to Know SkillBuilder, page 42

A. 1. hostile
2. expression

3. anger
4. uncertain
5. ashamed
6. drug
7. countless

B. 1. antibiotic
2. plagiarized
3. reconcile
4. provoke
5. insubordinate
6. innumerable
7. inhospitable
8. tentative

C. Students' poems will vary. Accept responses that accurately use at least three Words to Know.

Grammar SkillBuilder
Participial Phrases, page 43
(Answers will vary.)

1. Trying to become Americans, my sisters and I battled with our parents.
2. Having been threatened by other students, my sisters and I decided we didn't want to go to school.
3. Sitting on her side of the bed, my mother would make detailed drawings of her latest invention.
4. As my mother burst into my room, I cried out, having lost the delicate strand of thought I was putting on paper.
5. Annoyed by the interruption, I tried, nevertheless, to guess at her new invention.
6. Having seen something unbelievable in the paper, Mami let out a yelp.
7. My father, startled awake by her cry, thought immediately that they were not safe.
8. Pointing to the newspaper, my mother focused our attention on the suitcase with wheels.
9. Thinking she was doing me a favor, Sister Mary Joseph asked me to deliver the teacher's day address at school.
10. Inspired by Whitman's poems, I wrote the speech that enraged my father.

Daughter of Invention
Selection Quiz, page 44

1. Seeing her invention actually being sold proves to her that she should take herself seriously as an inventor. However, her family is unsupportive of her pursuit, and she decides to give up inventing.
2. She doesn't want to give the speech because she is self-conscious about her accent, and she thinks her classmates will dislike her for saying flattering things about the teachers.
3. Whitman writes about celebrating the individual, and he says that the best student learns to "destroy the teacher."
4. He is influenced by his memories of living under a dictator who punished with death any challenge to his authority.
5. Her mother's speech is polite and complimentary toward the teachers, but it is very ordinary and shows no imagination.

A Voice/The Journey
Active Reading SkillBuilder, page 45
(Responses will vary. Sample responses are provided for "A Voice.")
Word: unrelenting
Meanings and associations: harsh, cruel
Word: patriotism
Meanings and associations: love of country, flag waving, citizenship, pride
Word: spunky
Meanings and associations: spirited, lively, brave, never gives up

A Voice/The Journey
Literary Analysis SkillBuilder, page 46
(Responses will vary. Sample responses are provided.)
A Voice
Word Choice: forbidden
Definition of Word: not allowed
Other Words Poet Could Have Chosen: banned, outlawed, taboo
My Associations with the Word: dangerous, evil, tempting, leading to harsh punishment
The Journey
Word Choice: melancholy
Definition of Word: sadness
Other Words Poet Could Have Chosen: depression, gloom, unhappiness
My Associations with the Word: quiet sadness; a feeling that hangs over you and that you often can't identify
Follow Up: Students' ideas on what the word choice reveals about the author's perspective should reflect their understanding of the connotations of the words.

Building Vocabulary SkillBuilder
Denotation and Connotation, page 47
(Responses will vary. Sample responses are provided.)

1. The aroma of food filled the kitchen. The sneakers had a strong smell.
2. You should be particular about the company you keep. Picky eaters may not get the proper nutrition.
3. On the way to school, we would chat about this and that. When the winner was announced, everyone began to chatter excitedly.

4. We train new employees in the use of various software programs. Most schools educate students in language, science, and math.
5. He vowed his eternal love for her. A parent's work is endless.
6. She tried to imitate the movements of her coach. At a circus, the clowns sometimes mimic the acrobats for a laugh.
7. The starry skies filled us with childlike wonder. His childish demands for attention annoy everyone.
8. The two coaches had an argument about the umpire's call. The two senators held a public debate about campaign issues.
9. The house had a cozy, old-fashioned charm. The hospital needed funding to replace its outdated equipment.
10. Many young people leave their family for the first time when they go to college. The kittens will die if their mother has to abandon them.
11. He was ashamed of having cheated on the test. He was embarrassed at having forgotten the woman's name.
12. His parents should try to control his wild behavior. He learned to stand up for himself instead of letting others dominate him.
13. Please excuse me for being late. Please forgive me for hurting you.
14. Everyone enjoyed the unusual dish. The milk tasted peculiar, so I threw it out.
15. The severe cold didn't worry us, as we had an abundant supply of firewood. It was foolish to have bought such an extravagant amount of food for only three people.

Only Daughter
Active Reading SkillBuilder, page 49
(Responses will vary. Sample responses are provided. Differences in students' classifications of generalizations may make a worthwhile class discussion.)
Generalization: A girl's destiny is to become someone's wife./Overgeneralized
Generalization: The purpose of a girl's college education is to find a husband./Stereotyped
Generalization: Having sons is a source of pride; having daughters is not./Overgeneralized

Only Daughter
Literary Analysis SkillBuilder, page 50
(Responses will vary. Sample responses are provided.)
Theme
A parent's stamp of approval can be the key to a person's self-esteem.
Supporting Passages
"But the truth is, I wanted him to interrupt. I wanted my father to understand what it was I was scribbling . . ."
"In a sense, everything I have ever written has been for him, to win his approval . . ."
"He laughed at all the right places and read lines he liked out loud."
"Of all the wonderful things that happened to me last year, that was the most wonderful."
Theme
In order to fulfill themselves, people must not accept the stereotyped ideas that others may have about them.
Supporting Passages
". . . my father thought college was good for girls—good for finding a husband."
". . . my brothers felt it beneath them to play with a *girl* in public."
". . . my father shakes his head even now and says I wasted all that education."
". . . somehow I could feel myself being erased."

Only Daughter
Words to Know SkillBuilder, page 51
A. 1. fulfill
2. nostalgia
3. anthology
4. embroider
5. trauma

B. 1. trauma
2. nostalgia
3. fulfill
4. embroider
5. anthology

C. Students' sentences will vary. Accept responses that accurately use at least two Words to Know.

Only Daughter
Selection Quiz, page 52
1. Since her brothers wouldn't play with her, Cisneros had plenty of time to think, read, and imagine.
2. Her father didn't care what she studied, because he believed she was only in college to find a husband. Therefore, she was able to major in English instead of something practical.
3. He couldn't read English, and he wasn't interested in good literature.
4. Her father missed Mexico, and they would often move back there for a while.
5. Her father read a Spanish translation of one of her stories and liked it so much that he asked for copies to give his relatives.

from The House on Mango Street

Active Reading SkillBuilder, page 54

(Responses will vary. Sample responses are provided.)

How old is Esperanza?

Facts and Details from the Text: She has lived in several houses; her mother tells her to go to school and study hard; Esperanza is the oldest of four children; her father tells her about her grandfather's death so that she can tell the other children.

My Experiences and Prior Knowledge: Her father gives her a responsibility that a parent would probably not give to a very young child.

Conclusion: She is probably in her early teens.

What past experiences has she had?

Facts and Details from the Text: She has lived in several rundown buildings; a nun was shocked to see where she lived.

My Experiences and Prior Knowledge: It can be humiliating to have others feel sorry for you.

Conclusion: She has probably felt ashamed of being poor.

What are her hopes and dreams?

Facts and Details from the Text: Her parents promised that someday they would buy a beautiful house, but the house they finally bought is ugly; she wants to change her name; she likes to write stories; she plans to leave Mango someday but will come back for "the ones who cannot out."

My Experiences and Prior Knowledge: The story is based on the author's life.

Conclusion: She dreams of becoming a successful writer. She hopes to use her writing to help her family and community.

from The House on Mango Street

Literary Analysis SkillBuilder, page 55

Students' vignettes will vary but should provide a sketch of a home, family, or neighborhood.

Grammar SkillBuilder

Infinitive Phrases, page 56

(Answers will vary.)

1. The family decided to leave one flat because the water pipes burst.
2. Before we went to bed, mother told us stories about the house that she hoped to buy some day.
3. The nun from my school asked me to point out where I lived.
4. Mother likes to combine doing housework with listening to opera records.
5. To speak my name in Spanish, you make a soft, silvery kind of sound.
6. When my father told me of my grandfather's death, he started to cry.
7. Mother decided to quit school since she didn't have nice clothes.
8. My mother doesn't know which subway train to take downtown.
9. To write all of my stories on paper helps the ghosts fade away.
10. I want to pack my bags, to say good-bye, and to go away.

from The House on Mango Street

Selection Quiz, page 57

1. Esperanza had dreamed of a large white house with a big yard and trees, but the house on Mango Street is small, red, and in terrible condition. It has no front yard and a only a small backyard.
2. They both have the name Esperanza, and they were both born in the Chinese year of the horse.
3. Her great-grandmother was sad because her husband had forced her to marry him.
4. She puts her arms around her father and holds him for a long time.
5. Her mother wants her to be able to take care of herself rather than being dependent on a man.

On Writing *The House on Mango Street*

Active Reading SkillBuilder, page 59

(Responses will vary. Sample responses are provided.)

Important Details

"The voice . . . and all my work was born at one moment, when I realized I was different."

"In Iowa, I was . . . aware of feeling odd when I spoke, as if *I* were a foreigner."

"I felt ashamed when I spoke in class, so I chose not to speak."

". . . my political consciousness began the moment I recognized my otherness."

"Then it occurred to me that none of the books . . . in any of my classes . . . had ever discussed a house like mine."

"I got angry . . . I asked myself what I could write about that my classmates could not."

"When I teach writing, I tell . . . of discovering and naming my otherness."

". . . writing in a younger voice allowed me to . . . examine where [that shame] had come from and why, so I could exchange shame for celebration."

". . . the two halves of my lives [writing and helping the community] were at odds . . . since *Mango Street* has been published those two halves . . . have met and merged."

Main Idea

Cisneros's feelings of otherness led her to find her own voice as a writer and to help others in her community through her writing.

On Writing *The House on Mango Street*
Literary Analysis SkillBuilder, page 60
(Responses will vary. Sample responses are provided.)
Sentence Length: "Attic? My family lived in third-floor flats for the most part, because noise traveled down. Stairwells reeked of Pine Sol from the Saturday scrubbing."
Word Choice: Pine Sol; reeked; public zones; urban fauna; this guy Bachelard
Tone: The author uses short sentences and simple, ordinary words such as *guy* and *Pine Sol* because she wants to speak in the voice she is most comfortable with. Her tone is sarcastic, conveying the resentment that she felt when she was uncomfortable in the academic world for her "otherness."
Sentence Length: "writing in a younger voice allowed me to name that thing without a name, that shame of being poor, of being female, of being not quite good enough, and examine where it had come from and why, so I could exchange shame for celebration"
Word Choice: shame, not quite good enough, celebration; repetition of *of being*
Tone: The author's sentence is long, but her use of strong, simple words such as *shame* and *not quite good enough* and the repetition of *of being* send a passionate message—in a tone that conveys the embarrassment and shame that she once felt for being different.
Follow Up: Students' responses will vary but should demonstrate an understanding of how sentence length, word choice, and tone affect each writer's voice.

On Writing *The House on Mango Street*
Words to Know SkillBuilder, page 61

A.
1. evolve
2. affirmation
3. ingest
4. inception
5. presumption

B.
1. presumption
2. evolve
3. affirmation
4. ingest
5. inception

Sandra Cisneros uses a voice that is informal and personal in "On Writing *The House on Mango Street.*"

C. Students' lists will vary. Accept responses that accurately use at least two Words to Know.

On Writing *The House on Mango Street*
Selection Quiz, page 62

1. She felt that she was very different from the other students, and she was ashamed of the difference.
2. She realized that none of the books she had read in her classes were about people from a background like hers. She felt that the values and ideas she was being taught didn't reflect her own experiences.
3. She began writing about her own life, using language that was familiar and natural to her.
4. She wanted to examine and understand the shame she had felt in her youth. By naming the shame, she was able to get rid of it and feel good about herself.
5. Many of her readers have shared the book with their families, and they say that it tells the story of their life, too.